.93.

THE MEDITERRANEAN HEA⎯

Gilly Smith is a television researcher and journalist. She initially specialised in Third World issues before broadening her scope to include current affairs, film and food. She has researched programmes for BBC TV, Greater London Radio and Channel Four and is a regular contributor to *Taste* magazine and the TV columnist for *New Woman* magazine.

Rowena Goldman is a television producer/director and feature writer who trained as an actress before opting for journalism. She wrote for *The Scotsman*, *Time Out* and *Drama Quarterly* and then joined BBC Radio London as a reporter. She joined Thames Television where she produced programmes such as 'The Time . . . The Place', 'Visions' and 'AIDS Update '90' before moving to Channel Four as producer/director on the documentary series 'Food File'.

The Mediterranean Health Diet

The Delicious Way to Lose Weight and Live Longer

Gilly Smith and Rowena Goldman

HEADLINE

To Martin and Brenda, and Nesta and Bob

First published in 1993
by HEADLINE BOOK PUBLISHING PLC

10 9 8 7 6 5 4 3 2

ISBN 0 7472 4017 5

Illustrations by Pauline Little

Typeset by
Letterpart Limited, Reigate, Surrey
Printed and bound in Great Britain by
HarperCollins Manufacturing, Glasgow

HEADLINE BOOK PUBLISHING PLC
Headline House, 79 Great Titchfield Street, London W1P 7FN

Contents

Acknowledgements

Our research trips were only possible thanks to the hospitality of Maurice Barnouin and his wife Catherine at Domaine Gournier in the South of France, and Gianni and Damiana Calogiuri in Southern Italy. Thanks also to Roderick Cordara, Peter Parmigiani and Olivia Goldman for introducing us to them. Susie Haslam's Italian was essential in Southern Italy, and thanks as well to Ali Ridley for her Spanish and her encouragement.

Information came from many sources and inverviewees, but we're particularly grateful to Charles Carey at The Oil Merchant for his help with olive oils. Thanks to food stylist Rebecca Money for checking the recipes, wine buyer, Margaret Allen, and to Greater London Radio food critic Nigel Barden and the many sommeliers who gave their expert opinion on accompanying wines.

Thanks also to magazines *Wine and Spirit International* and *Decanter*.

The recipes were donated by the many remarkable chefs who have made this book so much more than a mealy-mouthed tome on healthy eating. Special thanks to Marco Pierre White for his inimitable assistance, and for introducing us to the young chefs who are changing the face of British cuisine.

Our literary agent, Andrew Lownie, secured our commission from Headline with awesome speed, and his ideas and support were greatly appreciated. Our biggest thanks go to Valerie Clegg who was always at the end of the phone ready to give nutritional advice and who checked through the entire text in her own time.

Introduction

Mediterranean, *health* and *diet* – three separate words which conjure up an image of sun, sea and sex fuelling potent holiday fantasies. Together they could mean an end to the famous British pallor, straining waistbands and notorious levels of heart disease. *The Mediterranean Health Diet* highlights how methods of eating to become slim and healthy can be a reality for the whole family.

Most of us would give up much to look as good as the sculpted, siliconed, false-eyelashed models who leer imperiously from the covers of fashion magazines. But in reality we can't live on lettuce leaves, so we sulk about it and take solace in another chocolate bar. As a result, half the adult population is overweight, our cholesterol levels are largely unchecked and, frequently, too high. Meanwhile, our National Health Service (NHS) is spending most of its money on curing diseases which are entirely preventable.

The food industry has responded by creating a line of diet foods which now sell faster than any other foods. Sales of low-salt, low-fat products rose by forty-four per cent between 1988 and 1990, but despite the fact that ninety-five per cent of people think that eating healthily is important, sixty-five per cent don't actually do anything about it.

Britain is a small island where, it seems, people have forgotten how to enjoy real food. We treat our palates with contempt and our bodies like machines. Among our other European neighbours, we're on our own in the dietitian's waiting-room. We're suffering from heart disease, cancers and bowel disorders; we prop up a laxative industry which simply doesn't exist in many countries; our psychological problems are increasingly manifested in eating disorders such as anorexia and bulimia; we eat out of boxes, diet on packets, drink out of cartons, then pop pills to wake us up and drink potions to put us to sleep just to maintain an equilibrium. We live in a country surrounded by water but eat our fish from sanitized, shrink-wrapped trays, or as take-aways, battered and wrapped to the extent that we cannot tell a fresh cod from a processed nugget. And the rest of Europe watches in amazement.

The old French philosopher, Brillat-Savarin, summed up the very simple truth when he wrote 'you are what you eat'. It's not as if the continental Europeans ever needed to be told. They have a completely natural relationship with food; to them it's as necessary as sex and siestas, and should be respected as such. While we're not suggesting that we should all take a nap on a cold rainy afternoon, we do understand our other needs, but not those relating to food. (The continental Europeans would argue that we have the same disrespect for sex and sleep, but that's another story.)

Sceptics in whose interest it is to stand by the sweets, fats and dairy industries argue that while we may be dying of heart disease in Britain, the Mediterraneans are dying of other illnesses at the same age. Their average life span of seventy-seven years is the same as ours. The difference is that while they're still active and healthy at seventy-six, we're on three pills a day to keep our heart ticking. Quality of life rather than quantity of years is what we should be after.

In a hundred years' time, this obsession with the way we eat will all seem very silly. Historically, we haven't always been stuffing ourselves with rubbish either. The war years, when rationing forced Britons to think twice about the food that was available, have often been quoted as the best diet we've ever had. But the period of gluttony following the Second World War which was supposed to rear strong young people to take us into a new age of prosperity, instead paved the way for unprecedented heart disease. As this became clear, nutritionists began to tell us what to eat and what not to eat in an attempt to get it right, and instead of making things better, it became worse and worse. Tabloids trumpeted the latest conclusions, about-turning with every latest fad until we became confused, disheartened and bored. At the same time our lifestyles were changing, and manufacturers saw a clever way to mass-produce our food, shove it in a box and invent the microwave to cook it. Over the years we've lost our relationship with the food of the land and the pan on the stove. But who cared; we were all liberated, suddenly free to watch more television. Today, one in five couch potatoes dies of diet-related diseases in Britain.

Changing our diet is no longer about losing weight to look better and achieve the look of a thousand billboard advertisements. We're suffering an epidemic of diet-related diseases in Britain and we have to do something about it, and fast. After smoking, heart disease is the biggest killer, and studies show that it is due to the way we eat. Fat used to be a feminist issue; now it's simply a drain on the economy. The NHS spends £500 million a year on people suffering from heart disease. Last year the Government produced a White Paper entitled *The Health of the Nation* which called a halt to this outrageous trend, giving firm indications of the nutrition guidelines which should be followed. The problem is that it is not a great read, and those people who send away for it are those whose job it is to decipher statistics or who are half-way there in changing their diet anyway. In *The Mediterranean Health Diet*, we've translated those guidelines for you, and have given a clear picture of the food we should all be eating to live a healthier, slimmer life.

The fact that this involves switching to a more continen-

tal European lifestyle, eating more fresh foods which grow
in the ground and on trees rather than those that drop off
an assembly line, is hardly bad news. Add to this the
evidence that taking time to eat with your family and
friends is the best bet for a less stressful digestive process.
Joining the European Community (EC) was planned as a
move towards political and economic stability; if we eat
like our overseas cousins, the new Community could save
many lives too.

So is this really a 'diet book'? Does it have recognizable
components as do the Hip and Thigh and the F-Plan
Diets? The answer is 'yes', the common factor being olive
oil. While we all know that copious amounts of this won't
help us slim, the Mediterranean Health Diet is about
more than faddy eating plans. Cooking the sorts of foods
we suggest will do more for a permanent weight loss than
will any amount of grapefruit breakfasts.

The central theme of this book is our relationship with
food. Our lack of respect for it means that we tend not to
know very much about it – the way to select the best
ingredients for our budget, the most nutritious and interesting ways to cook, and the most relaxing way to eat it.
Most of us grab a bite on the way to work and shovel
a burger down at lunchtime before racing around the
shops, and fix ourselves something to eat in front of the
television when we get home. Very little thought goes
into planning the most important element that keeps
us going and which can radically affect our everyday
performance.

Meanwhile, the tabloids thrust their headlines at us
over breakfast, boasting the latest 'discovery' in winning
the cellulite fight, finding the secret to eternal youth or the
remedy for rheumatism. A million books have been sold
revealing the cure for a thousand maladies, and virtually
all of them say the same thing, forcing us into a strait-
jacket way of eating.

Once we've stayed the course, we immediately fall off

the wagon and our bodies scream abuse at us as we chuck down another dustbin load of processed rubbish. Would you continue filling your car with meths after the first time it spluttered to a standstill? So why continue plying your ailing body with fats and sugars when your energy levels are laughable, you can't remember when you last saw your toes over that stomach, and your skin and hair look as depressed as you do? Food has everything that we need to give us optimum health. The sole job of the nutrients in our food is to make sure our bodies work properly, that we're energetic, protecting ourselves against the ravages of disease and infection and maintaining a good healthy weight. If you're tired, ill or overweight, the chances are that you've been poisoning yourself.

So, is this going to cost a fortune to put right? The best foods are the raw fruits and vegetables that cost the least. A tomato and an orange a day will certainly help to keep the doctor at bay, but they're also cheap, nutritious alternatives to the chocolate you crave when you need to boost your sugar levels in the middle of the afternoon. The Mediterranean Diet comes from a peasant diet, filled with the food of the land that the poorest people in Southern Europe grow themselves. Meat is very often not on the menu at all or, if it is eaten, it tends to be the leaner meat of the mountain goat or farmyard chickens which are used to running around all day. The fatty beef which comes from idle cows herded into covered sheds throughout the winter for controlled feeding might be tastier, but its fat is what nutritionists term 'saturated', and it's one of the most deadly contributors to heart disease. After years of indecision there is finally a consensus on what makes a good diet, and it's all rather embarrassing to realize that a good percentage of the global population have been on it for centuries.

The people who eat the best diet in the world also tend to have the closest families, and the highest regard for tradition. Most of them learn to cook at home, and grow up respecting the food which is the heart of family life. Across the Mediterranean, food is shared in an almost religious sense; in Morocco, a tagine or stew will be presented in a huge pot and each person will dip bread into it. In the lands where ancient myths established the stomach as the seat of the emotions, nourishment is well understood.

And our own role in promoting the Mediterranean Diet? We are not nutritionists. We are two journalists who worked on the first series of Channel Four's *Food File* in 1992, and were amazed at the level of interest in the programmes we made about the Diet. We found a family who switched to this from a regular fried feast, and lost a considerable amount of weight between them.

We're not interested in the concept of bringing our fat levels down to thirty-five per cent of total energy intake, as the Government's *Health of the Nation* White Paper puts it. What we need to know is *how* to do it. But most importantly, we believe it's time to forget about following the examples America sets us, and to learn from the way the continental Europeans eat. Eating healthily will get the body back on course, curing its ills and losing excess weight. Food, accompanied by exercise, gives us back our natural physique and the energy to live life as our bodies want us to.

Despite the horrific facts laid out in Chapter 1, we're not pessimistic about the future of the British diet. Lobbyists such as The Coronary Prevention Group, The Food Commission and Parents for Safe Food are putting pressure on the food industry and the Government to change their attitude, and to encourage greater availibility of cheaper fresh foods, but ultimately it's down to each individual to help him/herself. Already there are healthier foods in the shops, and that's because of the increase in demand rather than any moral judgement by the super-market bosses. This book celebrates food and is a backlash against the diet books which give tips on how to avoid eating. Filling up on a bowl of oats to avoid hunger during the day isn't practical for most of us and teaches us to treat food as the enemy. The message is simple – buy fresh foods, learn to cook again, and eat your way to a healthier Britain.

PART 1

The Mediterranean Diet

CHAPTER 1

Goodbye Greasy Spoon

The trouble is that eating, like sex, is a sensual pleasure and anyone wagging a finger at us in a 'nanny knows best' kind of way is likely to go down as well as a bowl of cold porridge. But unhealthy eating in this country has now reached epidemic proportions and, rather like the advent of AIDS, there is nowhere to run and nowhere to hide – digest the message and act accordingly, or suffer at your peril.

The Great British Diet is, quite literally, killing us and, given that the average household spends £45 a week on food – a fifth of total expenditure – we are paying for the pleasure. As Professor Philip James, Director of the Rowett Research Institute says, 'The average UK diet is currently so unhealthy that the whole population is at risk of unnecessary and preventable diseases.' The good news, though, is that we can now do something simple to make sure that we don't become members of the already over-subscribed Diet-Related Diseases Club.

IS THIS YOU?

Most people spend more time worrying about their weight than their health. You may be fed up with the spare tyre around your waist and the fact that your clothes don't fit; or you may be wondering where that second chin sprang from, almost overnight; or you may be one of those people who's just brutally honest with yourself – 'Face it, I'm fat'.

If it's any consolation, you're not alone. Every other person in Britain is overweight – that's half the adult population. If you weren't fat as a child, it's a shock to discover that once you leave your twenties behind, your body just doesn't do what it's been doing automatically for all those years – which is burn up food without you having to do anything.

Re-assessing your diet, which is what you now have to do, may seem like an uphill struggle. How to live without the daily doughnut and Sunday's bacon and eggs? And what about the weekly burger and fries on the way home from work? All you have to do is open your eyes; the truth is, however, that despite the enormous range of healthy foods which are now available, the average Brit is still stuck on packaged, processed foods, full of sugar, salt and 'hidden' fats, and prettily wrapped – at extra cost.

It's not just your waistline you should be concerned about, either. What goes tumbling into your trolley will be served up to what amounts to nothing less than a heart attack on a plate. One in four deaths every year is from heart disease caused by eating a diet like this. The tin and the take-away have come to represent the height of convenience, but at great cost to our constitution.

Wendy Doyle, Research Dietitian at London's Hackney Hospital says: 'Our reliance on being able to eat on the run is the chief culprit in our unhealthy diet. Processed and fast foods reduce our awareness and control over what we eat. We need to plan in advance what we're going to eat and make it a part of the day's schedule. Most people don't do this; they just wait until they're hungry and then eat whatever comes to hand. One of the problems is that eating is no longer a social family get-together, as it is in Italy, for example. Instead of grabbing fast foods, we should be sitting down to a proper meal.'

Dr Tom Sanders, a nutrition lecturer at London University, is even less mealy-mouthed. 'We're a nation of toothless, constipated fatties. More food eaten outside the

home equals high calorie foods equals overweight people.'
With hamburgers and chocolate available on every street
corner, is this any wonder?

You may not recognize yourself as you're reading this
because you may be one of a growing number of people
who have switched from butter to low-fat spread and from
full-fat milk to skimmed milk. It's a start, but it's not
enough. We still eat too many sweets, crisps, biscuits,
cakes, soft drinks and processed meats. Our sugar and salt
consumption is still rising, mostly due to manufacturers
putting them into processed foods, and our intake of
saturated fat, which is a major factor in increasing the risk
of coronary heart disease, is much too high.

Sweets and Snacks

Snacking and grazing has replaced more formal meals for
many people:

1989 – we ate £3.2 billion worth of sweets.

1990 – we ate £1.3 billion worth of crisps, nuts and
snacks = 8,129 million packets of crisps and nuts.

As for biscuits – we eat more of them than any other
country on earth.

FAT CHANCE OF LOSING WEIGHT

So, spam may be off, but chips, fry-ups, sticky buns and
greasy take-aways are, it would seem, still very much on.
We've read the shock-horror headlines and we know our
traditional diet is bad for us but, rather than looking for
the healthy alternatives, without hardship, we take refuge
in a national obsession based on abstinence – slimming.
We've had the F-Plan Diet, the Scarsdale Diet, the Mayo
Diet and are finally realizing that in the long run they
don't work for many people. They're all diet plans and it's

human nature, ultimately, to reject the routine and restriction these regimes place on what should be a pleasurable, as well as a necessary, experience.

At any one time, one in four adults in Britain is actively trying to lose weight but it doesn't seem to be having much effect. If you went in for the Beverley Hills Diet, the chances are you were still there for the Hip and Thigh. On top of this, we turn for help to a whole range of miracle diet pills and appetite suppressants even though they've already come under fierce attack by nutritionists.

Meal replacement products – biscuits and bars, mixes for drinks or other concoctions – are other refuges, but they offer doubtful nutrition and do little to help slimmers make the kind of dietary changes which will sustain a healthy weight loss. One of the biggest problems for slimmers is keeping the weight steady once it's been lost. This needs changes not just in the kinds of food eaten but also in eating patterns. Meal replacements and low-calorie diets do little to re-educate eating patterns, and so many diets are doomed to failure.

Meanwhile, as we diet, the food industry is laughing all the way to the bank. One half profits out of making us fat, and the other half gets fat out of making us slim. As long as there are diet junkies, there'll always be a fix.

FOOD FLASHBACK

It's ironic to think that during the war years, a time of deprivation and uncertainty, food policy in Britain actually worked. Vitamins – unheard of until the beginning of the century – and minerals like calcium and iron, became part of a mixed diet which emphasized protein – rich foods to promote growth as well as a ration imposed on fats and sugars. Children got taller just by eating moderate amounts of fresh food, or vitamin and mineral tonics and didn't get deficiency diseases. In cinemas up and down the country the authoritative voice of the Pathé news bulletin boomed the message home. The commentary accompanying one such report is pithy. A woman is seen sorting through her handbag 'looking for her complexion' and is next shown chopping vegetables to the words: 'An ounce of cabbage is worth an inch of lipstick.' Greens on screens made vegetables glamorous.

Dorothy Hollingsworth, who was a senior civil servant at the Ministry of Food during those years, says: 'Wartime food policy was an enormous success. Infant mortality, growth rates and dental caries (tooth decay) all improved. It was a surprise to all of us because, at the time, we didn't think that the imposed restrictions on fats and sugars were necessarily a good thing.'

Fats

As a general rule:

Saturated fats = solid at room temperature, except for palm oil and coconut oil.

Unsaturated fats = liquid oils.

Saturated fat = butter, lard, suet, full-fat dairy products, the visible fat on meat, and the 'hidden' fat in cakes, biscuits, pies, pastries, ice cream and chocolate bars.

Saturated fat causes heart disease.

Unsaturated fat, which is healthier, falls into two groups:

Polyunsaturated fat = safflower oil, sunflower oil, soybean oil, corn oil, walnut oil, grapeseed oil. Oily fish such as mackerel, herrings and sardines are also high in polyunsaturated fat.

Mono-unsaturated fat = olive oil, peanut oil, hazelnut oil and rapeseed oil. Duck and goose fat are also high in mono-unsaturated fat.

A mixture of polyunsaturates and mono-unsaturates is best.

Fat Tips

When you put butter on to hot toast it is absorbed so well that you never think you have enough on. So, you spread twice as much as you actually need. Try waiting until the toast has cooled down. That way you can see what you're letting yourself in for.

A wholemeal scone, with raisins to sweeten, is a good substitute for chocolate to satisfy your mid-afternoon craving.

KIDS IN A CANDY STORE

A process was already underway which turned into a roller-coaster after the Second World War. The buzz word was 'food technology' and it heralded a new age of cheapness and availability. White bread, mass-produced from flour ground and sorted in new steel roller mills, became big business; refined sugar grew from a molehill into a mountain, forming the basis of the new jam, biscuit, chocolate and confectionary industries; meat became everyday food for everyone now that mechanized slaughterhouses, rail transport and refrigeration were commonplace; canning and bottling gave manufacturers the chance to make staple processed foods from cheap ingredients; and hydrogenation, a process invented early this century, became a spectre which now looms larger than ever over the Great British Diet. This has turned unsaturated oils into hardened, saturated fat for the mass production of pies, pastries and biscuits. The British public embraced the new food revolution with open arms and is still locked in a loving relationship.

Hydrogenation = 'Hidden' Fats

Hydrogenation is used to convert healthier liquid, unsaturated oils into hardened, less healthy saturated fat.

Since vegetable fats can be produced much more cheaply than butter, the economic advantage of hydrogenation is obvious.

Hydrogenated fat is used to prolong the shelf-life of various baked products, as well as that of ice cream and chocolate bars.

The process is so widespread that it accounts for most of the 'hidden' fats in our diet.

Don't be fooled by the phrase 'hydrogenated vegetable oil' on the contents list of many snacks and convenience foods.

Low-fat Spreads

Low-fat spreads contain half the fat of butter or margarine and can be made of vegetable and/or animal fat. They vary in the amount of polyunsaturates and saturates they contain.

Reduced fat spreads = 60 per cent fat
Low-fat or half-fat spreads = 40 per cent fat
Very low-fat spreads = 20–25 per cent fat

Also on the market is a spread made with a fat substitute. This spread contains only 5 per cent fat.

Almost overnight, the British diet was transformed. One hundred and fifty years ago British food was mostly starchy; by the 1950s it was mostly fatty and sugary and promoted as cheap sources of concentrated energy. Postwar babies were brought up to believe that 'energy foods' were healthy and, since fats and sugars supply energy, that they were, therefore, nourishing.

A BRITISH WAY OF LIFE LEADS TO A BRITISH WAY OF DEATH

Even though wartime food policy was a proven success, scientists had, by the 1950s, begun to be worried by new epidemics of non-infectious diseases. Coronary heart disease was uncommon until the beginning of this century, yet by the 1950s it had become a major cause of premature death in many Western countries. And doctors working in Africa noticed that a number of non-infectious diseases (including heart disease), were unknown amongst people who ate traditional diets of unprocessed foods.

By the swinging sixties, many scientists noted that high blood pressure, diabetes, tooth decay, obesity, constipation and piles seemed to follow Westernization. They had been right before, though, in that a diet concentrated in animal protein, fats and sugars, promotes the growth of young people. What they didn't know then were the long-term ill effects of such an artificial diet.

So, the new findings presented a paradox: how could the same food that makes big, strong children cause disease and even death in middle age? Reports from expert committees of scientists were commissioned by governments and leading medical bodies in a number of Western countries. By the mid 1970s, most nutrition scientists accepted that the Western diet had become too fatty, containing, in particular, too much saturated fat which promoted the development of fatty deposits in the arteries of the heart.

Cholesterol

Cholesterol occurs naturally in the cells of all animals, including ourselves. It is made in the liver and is used to transport fatty acids around the body in the blood – hence the term *blood cholesterol*.

The danger comes when blood cholesterol levels are boosted by high intakes of foods high in saturated fat. The body then makes so much cholesterol that it can't get rid of it. It dumps the fatty, sludgy remains on the inner walls of the arteries, causing them to narrow or 'fur' up, restricting the supply of blood to the heart.

Foods low in saturated fat can still be high in dietary cholesterol which is only found in animal foods.

Liver, shellfish and eggs are low in saturated fat but high in dietary cholesterol. As dietary cholesterol has relatively little effect on blood cholesterol, however, as compared to saturated fat, most people don't need to worry about the amount of these foods in their diet.

Fatty meats, high-fat cheese and full-fat milk also contain dietary cholesterol; these foods are also high in saturated fat and should be limited.

The average level of blood cholesterol in Britain is 5.9 millimoles per litre – 5.9 mmol/L. A millimole is the measure used to show how much cholesterol there is in one litre of blood.

Experts agree that we should all aim to have a blood cholesterol level of less than 5.2 mmol.

Your GP can test your cholesterol level. He will also check the HDL level – high density lipo-proteins. The job of HDLs is to take excess cholesterol to the liver so that the body can get rid of it. So, the more HDLs, the better.

At first, attention focused on fat, saturated fat, sugar and dietary cholesterol. The reports recommended foods low in fat, and targeted sugar, which contains calories but no nutrients, causes tooth decay and makes fat palatable. Fatty, sugary food causes obesity which increases the risk of high blood pressure, diabetes and heart attacks. By the late 1970s there was consensus among scientists that everyone in Western countries would do well to eat less total fat and less hard, saturated fat and also to switch from saturated to unsaturated fat.

Calories

A calorie is simply a measure of heat energy – the amount of energy needed to raise 1g of water by 1 degree centigrade. Overloading our bodies with an excess of calories means more energy than we can use.

The energy we get from carbohydrates, fats and protein is either stored as body fat for later conversion, or burned up – 'metabolized' – to produce heat and muscular work.

Most of the carbohydrate we eat comes from potatoes, bread and cereal products like rice, and adding even a small amount of fat greatly increases the calorie intake.

A medium-sized baked potato with three pats of butter added makes the calories go up by 250 per cent.

We need different daily calorie intakes according to our age, gender and level of activity.

A one-year-old baby – needs about 1,150 calories a day.

A 12–14 year old boy – needs 2,650.

A 12–14 year old girl – needs 2,159.

A 15–17 year old boy – needs about 2,900.

A 15–17 year old girl – needs 2,150.

As adults, we no longer need calories for growing.

An inactive man with a desk job who doesn't take any exercise will need only 2,500 calories a day, but a man who takes moderate exercise will need at least 3,000.

An inactive woman will need 1,900 calories, but an active woman can use up to 2,500.

We gradually slow down our energy requirements with age, a woman's requirements slowing earlier.

The British Department of Health was drowning under a sea of these reports but together with the Ministry of Agriculture, they were happy to continue their unique commitment to food and agricultural policies originally devised in pre- and post-war Britain. This policy was designed not only to ensure security of supply but also to encourage production and, therefore, consumption of meat, milk and dairy products, and of cheap processed foods. They were, it seems, unimpressed by the evidence building up throughout the world which showed that, in common with other Western countries, the typical British diet was, and still is, a major contributor to serious diseases.

HORRIBLE TRUTH IS REVEALED

1983 was a ground-breaking year. The National Advisory Committee on Nutrition Education (NACNE) published a report which included dietary recommendations for the whole British population, not just those considered to be most 'at risk' of heart disease, obesity or malnutrition. It caused a sensation when *The Sunday Times* revealed that the report's findings had been suppressed. In common with most expert reports published outside Britain, it set targets with figures and put nutrition on the national agenda. But it took a national newspaper to highlight the significance of a report which was never fully endorsed by the Government.

In 1984, however, the Department of Health did publish a report by the Committee on Medical Aspects of Food Policy – *Diet and Cardiovascular Disease* – which *was* accepted as official Government policy. It accepted the world-wide scientific consensus on fat and heart disease and was the first UK Government-commissioned report to recommend targets, with figures, for the reduction of total fat consumption as well as saturated fats for the whole population.

1992 AND ALL THAT

The long-awaited Government White Paper *The Health of the Nation* again sets targets for fat consumption – to reduce from forty per cent to thirty-five per cent the total amount of food energy derived from all fat in the diet by 2000, and a lowering of energy derived from saturated fat from seventeen per cent to eleven per cent. It does not require food or farming industries to act, however, but promises to liaise with industry with the intention of reducing saturated fats, salt and sugar 'as far as practicable'. The rest, it seems, is up to us – and there's no excuse. In the 1990s, most British people have access to a real variety of healthy choices on the supermarket shelves. Wholegrain bread, low-fat milk and sugar-free breakfast cereals are lead lines.

Reading between the lines of the arid White Paper, the Government is recommending, as an alternative to what we've come to know and love, nothing less than a Mediterranean-type diet. As Mike O'Connor, who is a consultant to the World Health Organization (WHO), says, 'At last we're moving away from a policy of "Don't eat that" to one of "Eat more of this".'

CORONARY HEART DISEASE (CHD)

Every three minutes – the average time it takes to make a decent cup of tea – someone dies from coronary heart disease. Put even more starkly, that's the same as one jumbo jet crashing every single day and two each on Saturdays and Sundays. It's Britain's biggest killer, after smoking, but we never think it will happen to us.

There are various factors most associated with CHD called 'risk factors'. These are not the risks taken by bungee jumpers or mountaineers, but the risks taken every day – eating unhealthy food, smoking, lack of exercise. (Others include being overweight, stress and blood pressure. There are also risk factors over which we have no control, like age, sex and family history.)

And what about 'risk factor' trade-offs? 'I can't resist rich food and I know I need to lose weight, but I don't drink and I've given up smoking, so that's OK'. No, it's *not* OK. We're all very good at deluding ourselves, but as we don't know what triggers a 'risk factor' into a fatal event, there can be no cheating. We have to look at *all* the risk factors. White Papers and government policies should make lifestyle changes simple and possible but, in the final analysis, we must take life into our own hands. By the time you've read these three paragraphs, someone else will have died from coronary heart disease.

You're still healthy, however. Your blood flows easily through your coronary arteries, carrying blood to your heart muscle. There's nothing wrong with you. Nevertheless, if you're eating a diet full of saturated fat your arteries may already be starting the 'furring up' process without your realizing it. This means that they will be narrowing, building up fatty deposits.

A severe pain in the chest, known as angina, particularly felt when exercising, is a common symptom of CHD and is caused by the build-up of fatty deposits. You get a heart attack because of a blood clot forming at the site of narrowing, thereby blocking the artery.

The trouble with identifying the pain of CHD is that the intensity can vary enormously. It can be quite mild and feel like indigestion, or it can take the form of palpitations – the kind of thing you get if you've just lost your job or seen the love of your life across the street. At the other end of the scale, an excruciating crushing feeling can spread from the chest to the neck and arms. For some people, it's the last thing they'll ever know.

Cardiac Massage

The British Heart Foundation is very keen that everyone should know what to do if someone 'drops down dead' in front of them. If it looks like a heart attack, you can probably save this person's life if you follow these simple guidelines.

– Following a heart attack the victim will collapse. Within three minutes, the blood stops pumping to the rest of the body and, most importantly, to the brain, and the victim will die, or risk brain damage.

– Massage the heart and give the kiss of life, and the

blood supply will probably start again, and brain damage will have been avoided.

– Get someone to call an ambulance immediately. Thanks to the British Heart Foundation, all ambulances are now equipped with a defibrillator which sends a vital electric current through the heart to get it going again.

One other thing before we leave the subject of you and your heart. Don't think that if you're a woman you've been let off the hook. CHD and strokes are the leading causes of death in women aged 35–54, and these death statistics ignore the thousands of women who are disabled by CHD. At the moment, almost all the research on the causes and prevention of CHD has been conducted on men, and health education advice has tended to be aimed at men. If women *are* addressed it is often in their role as mothers and wives, advising them what they can be doing to reduce their husband's/partner's or children's risk of CHD. But women's hearts need looking after, too.

Where are You in the Heart-Attack Queue?

ON A SCALE OF 1 TO 100

With every beat of your heart, time ticks away – sixty beats a minute, sixty minutes an hour, every day of your life. In assessing the dangers inherent in someone's lifestyle, GPs now have access to a pocket risk calculator – the Dundee Coronary Risk-Disk – developed by Professor Hugh Tunstall Pedoe of Dundee University, endorsed by the Coronary Prevention Group and the British Heart Foundation. The doctor can 'dial' in relevant lifestyle factors which reply with an overall risk factor rating on a scale of one to one hundred. Each risk factor has a knock-on effect on the next. Here are some fictitious examples:

Name:	Bob
Age:	45
Smoker:	Yes – a 25 a day man
Blood Pressure:	170/105
Cholesterol Level:	7 mmol/L
Overweight:	Er, slightly
Exercise:	Not much
Diet:	Average

Bob is third in the queue for a heart attack. If all he did was to stop smoking for a couple of years, he would fall back to fifteenth place in the queue, that is, fifteen places from the front. If he kept on smoking but improved his diet sufficiently to reduce his blood cholesterol and keep it at a level of no more than 5.5 for two years, he would be thirteenth in the queue. If he stopped smoking, however, *and* improved his diet, he would slip right back to thirty-fifth.

Name:	Tom
Age:	60
Smoker:	No, never
Blood Pressure:	160/100
Cholesterol Level:	7 mmol/L
Overweight:	A bit
Exercise:	What's exercise?
Diet:	Below average

Tom's diet is high in saturated fats and this, plus all the other risk factors means that he is forty-sixth in the queue.

Name:	Ann
Age:	50
Smoker:	20 a day
Blood Pressure:	140/90 – that's average for a woman of my age
Cholesterol Level:	4 mmol/L – quite low

Overweight:	No
Exercise:	Some
Diet:	Healthy

Ann eats a healthy diet, high in fresh fruit and vegetables and low in saturated fats. Her smoking and blood pressure, however, lift her to forty-third in the queue – slightly ahead of Tom. If she had never smoked, she would be almost at the back of the queue – at ninety-seventh. So, remember – there are no trade-offs.

The person of around average risk is a man aged forty, who smokes twenty-five cigarettes a day, has blood pressure of 130/80 and a cholesterol level of 6. He eats an average British diet, isn't overweight and takes moderate exercise. This 'average' lifestyle puts him well forward in the queue at twentieth. If he gave up smoking now, he would drop back to eightieth. And if he had never smoked, he would be even further back in the queue at eighty-second. Better still, if he cut his blood cholesterol to 5.5 for two years, as well as giving up smoking, he would go back eight more places to ninetieth.

CANCER

After heart disease, cancer is now the biggest killer disease in most developed Western countries, killing one in five people. The Big C is more frightening to most of us than a heart attack; epidemiologists estimate that more than one-third of all cancers result from an unhealthy diet.

The potential connection between cancer and diet was first discovered some twenty years ago by Dr Denis Burkitt and Dr Hugh Trowell, who coined the term 'Western Diseases'. Their thesis was that foods rich in fibre protect against, most notably, bowel cancer, but also against many other non-infectious diseases and disabling conditions such as constipation, piles, tooth decay, hiatus hernia, gallstones and diverticular (intestinal) disease.

For an indication of how high or low your fibre intake is, try looking at stools – not the ones which line the bar in your local pub but the ones you deposit at the bottom of the lavatory pan. On his travels around the world preaching his thesis, Denis Burkitt discovered that when diets are rich in fibre, the stools passed are usually large, pale and soft, and often float. Stools associated with a low-fibre diet, however, are the exact opposite. A strained, red face in the smallest room in the house is likely to produce something akin to large rabbit droppings.

As a rule, fatty and sugary food is food poor in fibre because fibre is processed or 'refined' out of Western food. 'The food component that changes most with adoption of Western dietary habits,' says Burkitt, 'is the indigestible fibre. Four to five times as much fibre is consumed by rural communities in the third world as by Western populations.'

After smoking, diet is likely to be one of the major contributing elements to cancer, and 1992 saw the start of the world's largest ever in-depth investigation into this link. The European Prospective Investigation into Cancer (EPIC) involves seven European countries and over 250,000 people. 'It will go on indefinitely,' says Dr David Forman, one of the coordinators of the study, 'but we'll see the real fruits of the study in ten years' time.'

Cancer and Diet

It's been estimated that changes in diet might prevent as many as 35 per cent of cancer deaths.

For specific cancers, there are startling estimations of deaths possibly avoidable by dietary change:

90 per cent of large bowel cancer
90 per cent of stomach cancer
50 per cent of breast cancer

50 per cent of cancer of the pancreas

OBESITY

One in twelve men and one in eight women are actually obese. At the risk of offending some 'happy-to-be-fat' readers, fat parents are more likely to have fat children. This can be a genetic tendency, but bad dietary habits picked up in early life are far more likely to cause weight problems in adulthood. So it's essential to teach children good eating habits. Obese children have a tendency to respiratory illness, raised blood pressure and high blood cholesterol levels. Additionally, the seeds of CHD are usually sown in childhood. The bodies of Vietnam war victims – young men in their early twenties – were shown already to have a build-up of fatty deposits in their arteries.

Mike Raynor, of the Coronary Prevention Group, recognizes the problem of children's eating habits. 'Steering kids away from junk food can be difficult because of peer pressure. The answer is to negotiate. Children understand that.'

SO, FAREWELL

'A wonderful variety of culinary traditions from throughout Europe and indeed, from the rest of the world can contribute to a healthy diet,' says Professor Philip James, 'but we have almost forgotten our heritage of appropriate cooking skills'.

We can get them back again, though, just by applying the kinds of skills used by Mediterranean people on a whole variety of wonderful foods which are readily available in this country. The use of vegetables, oils, citrus fruits, herbs, garlic, spices, wines and vinegars which have developed in various Mediterranean countries is the key to a range of recipes and tastes without the need for dishes high in saturated fat, cholesterol, salt or sugar to refresh our jaded palates. Goodbye, greasy spoon.

Testimony

SUE AND ROGER

Sue and Roger were existing perfectly happily on their diet of fried foods, take-aways and chocolate before we persuaded them to give it up in exchange for their 15 minutes of fame on Channel Four's Food File. Roger, a desk-bound, business-lunching fatty of forty-two, had an alarming cholesterol level of over 8 mmol/L and weighed 12 stone (76.2 kg). Sue was a size 18, but had once been the image of her twelve year-old and very slim daughter, Lynsey. Fifteen year-old Sara was also a sylph-like beauty, but already cultivating the eating habits which had been the ruin of her parents. The whole family agreed to put aside their convenience foods, beer and sweets and go Mediterranean for Channel Four.

Over the eight required weeks, Sue and Roger lost a total of 3½ stone (22.25 kg) between them, and Roger's high cholesterol level plummeted 3 points. Their HDL (protective cholesterol) levels rose, and they vowed never to return to their old diet. They even found that their weekly shopping bill was down an average of £10 – from £68 to £58. They found the recipes extremely easy to follow and even rediscovered the pleasures of eating together as a family. With new-found knowledge about food, Roger was able to keep to his diet throughout his frequent business lunches, while Sue found she could replace her doughnuts with fruit scones. They had their problems, of course. Sue didn't realize that she wasn't supposed to be eating five scones a day instead of her one doughnut but, overall, they found it remarkably easy to change their whole diet forever.

CHAPTER 2

Buongiorno a la Sante, Que Aproveche y Kalin Orexi
(or, Eat it before it gets cold)

Britain is on its own among its European neighbours as being a nation of people who use food simply as a means to an end. Across the water, the French, Spanish, Greeks and Italians love their food with a passion that shows in the time they'll take to buy and cook it and serve it to their family and friends. The food grows plentifully, from North Africa to the costas of Spain, sweeping through Provence and the French Côte d'Azur down through Italy to Greece and Turkey, Lebanon, Israel, North Africa, and the islands of Sicily, Cyprus and Crete. No wonder that the people who live in this cornucopia of Mediterranean feasts are among the healthiest in the world.

Provence is one of the most famous of France's natural treasures. It stretches across the shores of the Mediterranean, up hillsides mottled with olive trees, across plains draped with sunflowers, towards the Alpes Maritimes in one direction and the Rhône Valley in the other. Garlic is its middle name, with *aïoli*, or garlic mayonnaise, its most famous son. The land is outrageously fertile; 'throw a tomato seed on a rock in Provence and it will bear fruit,' as Nico Ladenis, Provençal resident, masterchef and owner of London's Chez Nico, Simply Nico and Nico at Ninety, told us.

As well as ripening the food, the sun dictates the day's activities. The midday heat forces Mediterraneans indoors and encourages lengthy lunches in the cool of the shade. Just outside the ancient Roman town of Nîmes, on the borders of Provence and Languedoc, business doesn't stop for lunch at the vineyard of Domaine Gournier.

We could learn a thing or two from these people; Maurice Barnouin and his wife Catherine are preparing lunch while their wine tasters discuss the blending of the reds which will produce one of next year's wines. It's the sort of conversation which could be overheard in a packed wine bar in any city in the world. The difference here is that nobody's looking at their watch, nobody's tugging at a stiff collar, and all attention is on the olive oil marinade Maurice is preparing for the tuna steak. Work starts early at Domaine Gournier; at 6 a.m., Maurice is in his fields, and can take a break to do the shopping by 11 a.m.

At the daily market in Nîmes, we wander through stall after stall of fresh fruit and vegetables while Maurice discusses his choice of fish and olives with the stall holders. It's a far cry from the nudging of shopping trolleys in the cereal aisle at Tesco's where the emphasis is on getting in and getting out as soon as possible.

The tuna steak has now been marinating in the local extra virgin olive oil and sea salt for half an hour, and Maurice blasts it under the grill while Alain and Maryse, the wine consultants, finally persuade him of their choice of blends. Catherine skins the red peppers which have been scorched under the grill, slices them and covers them with more local olive oil and tiny slices of garlic. The feta and tomato salad and a glass of red encourages the conversation to move on to the exporting of the wines abroad. Now *this* is what we call a working lunch. Two hours later, business is finished and it's time for a siesta. They start early and finish late in the Mediterranean, and we can't help but think that it's not so much the heat that they're working around, but the food.

Further south, Greece and its arid islands positively squelch with olive oil and ripe fruits, swollen by the unrelenting sunshine. Spanish markets and North African *medinas* bustle with daily shoppers bargaining for a best price for their vegetables. In these countries, it is the rich who are the worst off, who have the disease and the large gut. It is the trendy who are adopting the fast food of the British and the Americans, and the peasant farmers who continue to eat the food and drink the wine of the land. And it is this basic diet which nutritionists believe is the healthiest in the world.

Experts have been trying to prove their suspicions about the diet in this area for decades. The problem had always been that the lifestyle was so much more relaxed that there was less likelihood of the people keeling over from stress-related heart attacks. Slowly though, the correlation between eating natural foods and healthier hearts became clearer. It began as a gentle muttering, and quickly grew to become a new buzz word in the nutrition world. The press has been quick to hype it, the supermarkets have been anxious to apply it to sales, and the World Health Organization has endorsed it as the way forward into the new millenium.

One of the most famous of the studies took its workers all over the globe, and concluded in a little village on a hillside in Southern Italy.

To find the people whose hearts are among the healthiest in the world, we took a trip through some of the most breathtaking scenes in Europe.

AL ITALIA

Italy, and the Amalfi Drive is said to be the most beautiful coastal stretch in the Mediterranean. The corniche weaves through mountains which plunge abruptly into the Tyrrhenian Sea forcing gasping tourists round hairpin bends to the south, and to Campania. Its almost Caribbean scenery has been the playground of artists, poets and aristocrats for centuries, while its biggest city, Naples, with its noisy, overcrowded and poverty-stricken charm, is the second biggest port in Italy.

Spring in Acciaroli, a little port town south of Salerno, offers a balmy serenity, a lull before the invasion of frankfurter-feasting Northern European tourists. The annual flurry of activity which transforms its restaurants and bars into a banquet fit for heart patients is quiet now; hoteliers doze in the spring sunlight and ignore our pleas for service, while the gentle roll of the waves soothes our cityfolk impatience.

It is this quiet corner of Southern Italy which is where some of the world's most prestigious nutritionists have chosen to end their days. Campania is said to have the best diet in the world. Here in the rolling hilltop villages experts agree that the locals are least likely to die of diet-related diseases. Why? In a word or two, olive oil. Here, people drink the stuff for breakfast. After all, they tell us, it *is* only fruit juice. The murmur of the village tractor as it makes its way down the mountain, and the chatter of the village elders ambling to the café in the midday heat, drown the feverish debates and sales pitches echoing around the cities of the world. Their diet has become big business, and they don't give a damn.

One in five people in Britain die of diet-related diseases. A higher risk of arthritis, gallstones, appendicitis, heart disease and some cancers is the result of poor eating, high saturated fat intake and a slothful couch potato lifestyle. While the NHS buckles under the strain of reduced funds, the Government is keen to encourage the public to tighten their belts and shift those health-threatening extra tyres.

Nutritionists have been studying the effects of diet on our health for years. The *Seven Countries* study led by the American Professor, Ancel Keys, set out to look at lifestyles across the world to examine their links with local diseases. Food, it concluded, was the common ingredient in a melting-pot of living conditions which affect our health. The one area where people were not keeling over from heart attacks, or dying of bowel and breast cancer, was the rural area of the Mediterranean. Here the poorer members of the community were living off the land, eating food from trees and fields rather than out of a cardboard box. And, most importantly, they were eating olive oil.

This is the food on the tables in Celso, a village nestling among the olive groves in Campania's hills above Acciaroli. The home-made pasta, and tomato sauce, made with extra virgin olive oil from the press next door, have given the community among the healthiest hearts in the world. In an on-going world-wide study, coordinated by the Institute of Nutrition in Rome, they have been tested every ten years for diet-related diseases.

Professor Anna Ferro-Luzzi is in charge of the study, and is back in Celso to meet up with her test families. In a world away from Rome, she is stopped every few minutes by villagers who want to shake her hand; she knows their names, their family history and their cholesterol levels. The likelihood of their hearts, oiled by their own olives over decades, to become diseased as is as small as the likelihood of a McDonald's drive-in in this rustic scene.

Ferro-Luzzi and Ancel Keys, author of *Eat Well and Stay Well*, have put this unassuming hilltop village on the nutrition map. Through a process of elimination the *Seven Countries* study concluded that diet was largely to blame, and narrowed down the little island of Crete as having the healthiest in the world. Meanwhile, in the North of Europe, Finland was becoming an area of serious concern where a third of its middle-aged population was dying of coronary heart disease. Keys was one of the first to call it an epidemic, a term which was not taken seriously in the profession. 'The message simply wasn't being received either by the victims or by doctors,' he told us. 'But we were becoming convinced that there was mileage in studying the correlation between heart disease and diet. It seemed that the richer members of every population were the likely targets of disease, and after eliminating the differences in lifestyle, we decided that it had to be because they were eating richer foods with more dairy products. It was simply a matter of putting two and two together, and then persuading the medical profession that we'd found the answer.'

That took some time. Even after Anna Ferro-Luzzi's 1960s study analysed the food intake in sixteen Mediterranean countries and discovered the nutritional relevance of the classical diet on which its people had been surviving since 2000 BC, the findings were still greeted with scepticism. Eighty-nine-year-old Professor Keys has waited nearly fifty years for his conclusions to be the focus of the nutrition world, and finds the sudden interest symptomatic of the mood in the medical profession. 'It's taken them a long time to accept it, and longer to do anything about it,' he complained. 'Top cardiologists all over the world poured scorn on our findings, preferring to wait years for epidemiological studies to prove the same thing. All doctors do is look at their heart attack patients and find a way of curing them. What about encouraging them to prevent the things in the first place?'

Keys has joined a band of elderly nutritionists who have put their money where their mouths wanted to be, and moved into the Campanian coastal village of Pioppi. The octogenarian says that he wants to end his days with sundrenched fruits and vegetables on his doorstep, with fish arriving daily in the tiny local port, and with olives quite literally cascading down the hillside. He and his wife live on a clifftop surrounded by a modest few acres of olive groves, and a vegetable garden producing everything they could ever want to eat. 'Having it all literally on your doorstep can get a bit boring though,' confessed eighty-two-year-old Margaret Keys who will make the trip to the local shop to buy spinach when the home-grown artichokes and broccoli become too much of a good thing.

Their neighbour is the former Surgeon General of

THE MEDITERRANEAN HEALTH DIET   41

Finland, Martti Karvonen, who was one of the few to take seriously the Professor's claims about an epidemic in Northern Europe. An important programme was launched, albeit slowly, and Finland is now exemplary in its successful application of a food policy. In 1985 a national strategy plan was adopted which gave executive authority for the translation of these nutritional guidelines into actually controlling the food supply. In short, it was going to become too expensive and too difficult to buy the food which had been killers.

The Finnish National Food Plan

– To ensure a sufficient, balanced and varied diet
– To rely on domestic production of fish, cereals, potatoes, vegetables, berries, low-fat meat and dairy products
– To reduce sugar and salt-dense foods

The results have been phenomenal. Studies between 1987 and 1989 show that over three-fifths of the Finnish people now drink low-fat milk, two-thirds eat fresh vegetables frequently, just about everyone eats black or brown bread and more than half eat low-fat spreads, poultry, fish and fruits.

So the Finns have a more switched-on Government, and the likes of Ancel Keys can afford to buy his dream home in the heart of the world's best food land. But how can the Mediterranean Diet work in Britain? Luckily, where there's a buzz word, there's generally a salesperson, and the market has been flooded with an enticing selection of olive oils, pastas and Mediterranean goodies. Spanish tapas bars have become the Wimpys of the nineties, and supermarkets can now provide us with fresh fruits from all over the world throughout the year. If you live near a supermarket, you might well feel as though you are living in the Mediterranean.

While the all-important layout of the stores may lead us straight to the seductive delights of the colourful and sweet-smelling fruits and exotic vegetables, the food industry isn't, however, putting all its eggs into one shopping trolley. Fractious mothers curse the designers who put the sweets next to the check-out and crisps and biscuits at toddler level while those of us who believe the advertisements which tell us we don't have time to cook, turn the corner from the fruit and vegetables to be confronted by a gala of boxed cook-chill meals. 'Eat to your heart's content' scream the billboards, ensuring us that we can liberate ourselves from a life of domestic hell. Food in a box? Next, we'll be freeing ourselves even further with nutrition pills from a dispenser. And what do we do with all this extra time anyway? We watch television.

The Government's White Paper *The Health of the Nation* claims that a higher intake of fibre, fruit and vegetables, and less fat in our diet will reduce the appallingly high numbers of coronary patients, and limit the cases of breast and bowel cancer in this country. But while the Department of Health is publishing glossy reports and posturing about prevention of disease, the Ministry of Agriculture, Fisheries and Foods is busy protecting the needs of the food industry. Saturated fats may have been proved to be one of our biggest killers, but while hospitals in Britain still receive an eighty per cent subsidy on butter and milk and farmers are paid more for fatter cows, how are we to be given the choice when money talks louder than any buzz word?

Ironically, with the might of the Northern European food industry weighing down on the European trade barriers as they finally give way, the Mediterranean Diet may itself be under threat. Statistically, it's the poor who are the suckers for the sweet and processed food industries. Fast food chains loom ominously on an ever-widening horizon. While we may be wising up to a better diet, if the tentacles of the food industry creep south to strangle the local markets of the Mediterranean, we'll have to watch disease attack the heart of the world's healthiest people.

As spring gives way to summer this year, the smell of chips and frankfurters will begin again to pervade Campania's tiny tourist resorts of Pioppi and Acciaroli. Far enough perhaps for now to escape the sensitive nostrils of the band of elderly nutritionists, but how long can it be before greed for tourism's riches eats into even the healthiest hearts?

(Part of this text first appeared in an article on 'The Mediterranean Diet' by Gilly Smith in *Taste* Magazine April 1992.)

CHAPTER 3

Well Oiled

Olive oil has been singled out as the most important ingredient in the fight against heart disease. Not surprisingly, it has to be eaten within a well-balanced diet to obtain the maximum effect; there's no point in living on chocolate and olive oil and expecting to live to 100. In this country, people either love it or hate it, and many of those who say they hate it have never tried it. It is associated by some with holidays in the sun and by others as 'foreign muck'. In this chapter, we hope to explain why it's being heralded as the answer to our health problems, and to introduce you to its wealth of flavours.

Olive oil comes from all the countries in the Mediterranean and reaches markets all over the world. It has been in Britain for years, but until fairly recently was to be found nestling between the Alka Seltzer and the bicarb on the chemist's counter. Our grandmothers used it for strengthening nails and hair and for digestive disorders, but rarely in food. Now nutritionists are claiming that as a population for whom heart disease has reached epidemic proportions, we should throw ourselves wholeheartedly into the European Community and get cooking.

Granny's (somewhat extravagant) Olive Oil Remedies

For shining hair – Mix olive oil, lemon juice, egg yolk and beer and leave on dry hair for 5 minutes. Rinse and shampoo as normal.

To prevent dandruff – Mix olive oil with eau de cologne and leave on hair for 5 minutes. Rinse.

For dry skin – Mix avocado and olive oil into a face mask and leave on the skin for 10 minutes before rinsing.

To prevent a hangover – Drink a couple of spoonfuls before drinking (our researchers swear that this doesn't work).

To cure high blood pressure – Boil 24 olive leaves in 8 fl oz (250 ml) water for 15 minutes. Drink the liquid morning and night for two weeks.

For acne – Rub 8 fl oz (250 ml) olive oil and 10 drops of lavender oil on skin.

For weak nails – Soak nails for 5 minutes in olive oil and then paint with white iodine.

Olive oil is still used in the Roman Catholic church for baptisms. And if you don't substitute saturated fats in your diet, take heart from the fact that Catholics also use olive oil for last rites.

Dr Serge Renaud is one of the doctors whose studies have been at the forefront of the debate and who has, more than most, been responsible for clarifying the central components of the diet. His research on heart attack victims overwhelmingly shows that the Mediterranean Diet is a lifesaver.

THE LYON STUDY

Renaud's patients were living in one of the gastronomic capitals of Europe, Lyon, when they had their heart attacks. He asked 500 of them to take part in a study at the city's Hôpital Cardiovasculaire to examine the curative properties of a Mediterranean diet. Two hundred and fifty of them were asked to stick to a diet high in polyunsaturates, the diet normally prescribed by doctors to coronary patients, while the other half were weaned off their butters and creams, and reintroduced to the cleaner taste of fresh fruits, vegetables, fish, red wine and above all, olive oil. Having discovered through a process of elimination that the island of Crete had one of the world's healthiest diets, he wanted to prove that certain properties in its foods not only prevent these sorts of illnesses but can cure people who almost certainly would have had a second heart attack.

'The study began when we realized that the diet we had been prescribing for heart patients in both Britain and France wasn't working satisfactorily', Renaud told us. 'We were beginning to have evidence that a Mediterranean type of diet would be more efficient, at least in the population that was investigated. The only way to prove this was to change the diet of coronary patients who had suffered one heart attack, and to see if we could demonstrate the beneficial effect of the Mediterranean-type diet. The previous diet we'd set which was high in polyunsaturates and low in saturated fats wasn't achieving what we wanted.

Renaud's Six Commandments

More Bread
More Vegetables
No day without fruit
More fish
Less meat and more poultry
Mono-unsaturated fat (olive oil) instead of saturated fats

Renaud had a special margarine designed for the study, a mono-unsaturated fat with a balance of polyunsaturated fatty acids. The margarine was suggested for use instead of butter and cream, and olive oil became the main cooking oil. He explained how the use of fresher ingredients steered the patients into cooking completely different meals. 'When you're eating more vegetables and fruit, you don't tend to eat as much pastry, meat and saturated fat. You're more likely to think about a series of cheaper, more vegetable-orientated dishes than the meat and two veg we've all been used to in Northern Europe for so long.'

These fresh foods boosted the level of vitamins in the blood which had been shown to play an essential role in the prevention of a secondary heart attack. The body has its own repair mechanism which is serviced by a proper diet. Nutritionist Valerie Clegg explains 'Let's imagine that our network of arteries are the body's version of what planners might have dreamed the M25 to be. The body's lipoproteins are the cars which transport the fat around the body, but as there's a lot of water on the road, and water and fat don't mix, we need to break the fat down to avoid any skidding. Each lipoprotein contains a detergent which ensures that the fats don't crash into one another. No traffic jams mean easy circulation and unobstructed arteries. Unobstructed arteries mean no heart attacks. To take the metaphor further, the anti-oxidants become the car windows which prevent pollution from disturbing the natural equilibrium. Stop replenishing the stocks by leaving essential vitamins out of our diet, and we've left the windows open, and let the goodies get out.'

As well as looking after our own repair systems, we have to ensure that the food we eat is at its optimum condition too. Food is oxidized when cells are cut and oxygen is allowed in; see how an apple turns brown when cut in two. Luckily, there are plenty of ingredients which act as anti-oxidants and do this easily as well as extremely tastily. When added to fish, rosemary will prevent oxidation, and lemon squeezed on to a sliced apple will stop it from going brown. Cooking as much food as possible in extra virgin or virgin olive oil, will, accordingly to Renaud, avoid heart disease. 'It shows how Mother Nature looks after our needs. An olive is better for us than the refined oil we produce from it. A nut is better for us than nut oil. In the Mediterranean, people have a high consumption of these things. It's a shock to scientists like me to have to admit that Mother Nature knows best, but she does'.

Renaud will have to wait until the end of the study period before he can be absolutely sure, according to epidemiological guidelines, but he's optimistic about having found an answer. 'It just has to be positive,' he told us. 'It has yet to be confirmed by other groups, but I think we have to encourage a change in the diet behaviour of everyone. All heart patients will be prescribed this diet, but I think that it will appeal to the general population as well. And the changes are not too drastic either; it's OK to eat soft cheese, yoghurt and skimmed milk, so it's not all dairy products that we're criticizing. The good thing about it is that people will stick to it because it's so delicious.'

So does this study mean that we've been given the wrong information by the polyunsaturate groupies? Dr Renaud explained: 'Previously we'd been playing Sorcerer's apprentice because nobody in the world had stuck to a diet high in polyunsaturates. In the Mediterranean though, in Crete for example, there are a number of populations which have the greatest life expectancy in the world and follow one particular type of diet. I don't think that we were taking any risks in asking our patients to copy this diet. It's not that we were dismissing the positive effects of polyunsaturates, it's that we've discovered the link between a long and healthy life and mono-unsaturated fat such as rapeseed or olive oil.'

Testimony

MICK KIDD

Mick Kidd, writer of the BIFF *cartoons featured in the* **Weekend Guardian,** *suffered from gallstones a couple of years ago. He was forty-two and eating a high saturated fat* *diet when he was diagnosed after suffering intense pain. He switched to a diet low in fats, but the hospital insisted that he have an operation. Trying alternative routes, he went to an acupuncturist, who showed him an article about 'the olive oil flush' in a magazine. He sent Mick to see a herbal practitioner on whose advice he drank a bottle of extra virgin olive oil. The stones passed through painlessly. Just to make sure that they really had gone, he had an x-ray, and the doctors were amazed to confirm that the olive oil seemed to have done the trick. He is now a firm fan of the Mediterranean Diet and has taken it further, eating no animal products, butter or eggs. 'The only thing I miss', he told us, 'is the smell of roast lamb.'*

Mick's herbal practitioner warns that although this worked for him, it's not something you should do without consulting an expert.

What, though, do we know about the little fruit which has caused such a stir in the nutrition world? The olive tree has a peculiar place in history. Its branch has come to signify a peace offering after centuries of expansive Mediterraneans spread their fruit over new territories. Some believe that the first olive appeared in Ancient Palestine with Egyptian records showing trading as far back as 6,000 years ago with the Palestinians. The olive tree has a lifespan of between 300 and 700 years, and there are even claims that a tree still standing in Israel was bearing its first fruit while Jesus was performing miracles.

Storing Olive Oil

If you buy the large 4 litre (7 pint) cans of olive oil, decant into bottles and store in a cool dark place.

Light will raise the acidity of the oil and make it go rancid.

Spain, the world's leading olive producer, probably received its first olive trees from the Carthaginians during their occupation in the fourth century BC. The Romans who later staked their claim, exported vast quantities back to Rome, and Spain's principal export market to this day is still Italy. The Greeks traded their oil for corn and precious minerals and peasants were even encouraged to pay their taxes in olive oil during the Venetian occupation in the Middle Ages. Greek poets celebrated its healing qualities, and the largely inhospitable soil and climate where the olive trees flourish have lent the fruit a mystique. The Greeks see it as a symbol of their own fertility and spirit in the face of centuries of invasions and earthquakes. It was their ancestors, the Phoenician Greeks, who took the olive tree with them to France in about 6000 BC, and planted it in what is now Marseilles. With the arrival of the olive-loving Romans, it spread throughout their first province in the Alps, which they called Provence.

Paul Fray is the president of the local oil and wine cooperative in the tiny ancient village of Sommières in the South of France. While the locals were bringing his workers their olives and wines for pressing and blending, he was travelling across the country, driving all day and eating in expensive restaurants every night. The rich food of the North was a treat he allowed himself, and relatively soon he was eating out more than at home. The cream, heavy sauces and lack of exercise gave him his first heart attack. A second one quickly followed, and the scar across his chest bears testimony to the horrific operations which gave him another chance.

His doctor ordered him on to an olive oil diet and warned that if he didn't take advantage of the healthy foods under his nose he wouldn't survive the year. Now at fifty-seven, Paul is fit, trim, taking regular exercise and eating his home-grown food.

Despite the plentiful olives in France, Greece, Spain and the other countries lining the Mediterranean coasts, it is Italy which is synonymous with olive oil for most people in Britain. Its claim to the first olives is well founded with records of trade between Sicily and the mainland in the sixth century BC, and it was the influence of the Italians which took the trees across borders throughout the Mediterranean. The invention of the screw press which yielded the first oil was theirs, and a legacy of feasting and culinary imagination has ensured that the Italians have the edge on others in their claim to the olive. While Northern Europeans made dutiful pilgrimages to Florence ostensibly to see the art, it was the food those first tourists took home, and the olive made yet another conquest on a new territory.

Each country produces a very different tasting oil, although the method of its extraction is based on the same practice devised by the Italians 2,000 years ago. In most cases, farmers will harvest their olives for their families and give the rest to the local cooperative mill. In many parts of the olive-bearing countries, the old stone mills have been replaced by a hydraulic machine which has stepped up production, and reduced its cost. While hand picking is, however, still the only reliable method of harvesting, olive oil will never be cheap.

Cooking with Olive Oil

Charles Carey is a connoisseur of olive oils at The Oil Merchant in London, and has the most inspiring number to choose from. He explained to us a few basics about getting the best out of the oils.

– Use olive oil, rather than the more highly flavoured virgin or extra virgin, for mayonnaise and for frying. You can heat olive oil to a temperature of 210°C/410°F before it will burst into flames, so you can fry most foods in it. The Spanish deep fry in it.

– Virgin and extra virgin can have a much stronger flavour. Use them to flavour foods such as salads or roast chicken and vegetables, which benefit from the added taste.
– Estate oils have a wide variety of flavour. They are expensive, but make a great difference to a special dish.
– Don't refrigerate the oil – it will become dense and cloudy. It won't harm it though, and the colour and clarity will return once it has been removed from the fridge. Good oil should, however, be treated like wine, and kept in a cool, dark place.

The hills below the village of Celso in Southern Italy's province of Campania are littered with the green and russet netting which lies beneath the olive trees, restraining their ripe fruit from cascading down the mountain to the little port town of Acciaroli. As far as the eye can see, villagers are gathering their harvest, bodies bent double across the hillside to collect the fallen fruit, others clambering into the trees to whack the stubborn remainder from the branches. Throughout the Mediterranean, the olive harvesters are at work between September and March, waiting for their local fruit to reach just the right point of maturity for the variety of oils they produce. Some olives will be picked when they are still green for sale as table olives, chosen for their firm flesh, while most of the oilier, riper black olives will go to the mill for pressing.

Table Olives

Green olives are gathered when they are immature and then steeped in a solution of potash to remove the bitterness. They are then preserved in brine.

Black olives are the ripe fruit which are sweeter and contain more oil. They can be eaten with salads, on their own or used to make stuffings.

Both black and green olives can be mixed with garlic, anchovies, and stuffed with almonds or pimentos and eaten raw.

When bought loose, pack olives in jars and cover with olive oil. The less flavoursome but cheaper groundnut oil is a good alternative.

Olives are not stored for long before pressing because the oxidation will not only deprive them of their goodness, but they will also ferment and become unsuitable for the oils. The fruit is washed to remove impurities, and then crushed and piled on to woven hemp mats, stacked and pressed to extract the oil.

In Celso, the village *frantoio* (olive-press) gently hums on the hilltop as its workers clear the old *sanza* or pomice from the last pressing and make way for a new load to produce extra virgin olive oil. The bottles in every kitchen there belie the traditional British view of olive oil. Unlabelled, and untinted, they are a far cry from the elegant 'objets' available on Waitrose's shelves. Olive oil in Italy has no pretentions; it's a way of life, providing most villagers with work, food and, above all, health.

In most parts of Italy, the presses are high-tech sparkling aluminium machines. In the little *frantoio* in Celso the stone mill still grinds the fruit, producing the *sanza* from which the oil will flow. The Celso press serves the village and its environs, and rejects the pomice, the mulch of squashed olives, after the oil has been extracted. This is first cold pressed olive oil and very probably virgin or extra virgin, although as it is used for local consumption, nobody is likely to test it. The grading is carried out by EC inspectors and refers to the level of acidity in the oil. Extra virgin is the best olive oil, and contains less than one per cent acidity, while virgin has less than two per cent.

The rest of Italy gives its oil to the world. The hydraulic machines are so advanced these days that one pressing can extract all the oil. In the past, and in some of the few villages like Celso where a stone mill is still used, fifty per cent of the oil would be extracted from the first pressing. Water would be added and then a further two or three presses would produce more oil. A centrafuge separates the water and oil, and the green liquid is then stored and distributed among the locals. If the oil is to be sold outside the community, is subject to grading, and fails the acidity test, the pomice would be sold on to be refined. This, when blended with other refined oils, and a little virgin for taste and colour, is the oil which we find in abundance on our supermarket shelves marked 'olive oil'.

Before we put on the Pavarotti and down a glass of Chianti, we shouldn't, however, be deceived by appearances. A product of Italy might simply refer to where the oil was mixed, and can contain a blend of oils from Greece and Spain. Nevertheless, the Italians are probably the best blenders in the world and with groves primarily serving the local need, they are crucial to a burgeoning industry in the North where there aren't too many olives to go around. 'The Italian dominance of the market is largely due to hype,' Charles Carey told us. 'They certainly are the best blenders, but most of the good cheaper oils are Spanish. The Northern Italians spend a good deal of money promoting their oils, and laying claim to the Mediterranean Diet, but in fact there are many interesting and cheaper oils in France, Spain and Greece.'

Henrietta Green's Guide to Supermarket Oils

Henrietta Green is a food journalist who conducted a survey on supermarket olive oils for the *Weekend Guardian* in the summer of 1992. These were her favourite extra virgins:

Asda – £2.15 500ml/ £2.49 750ml. Slightly watery, thin flavour, lacking in fruitiness with a peppery kick.

Marks and Spencer – £2.39 500ml Rounded rich flavour. Mellow but vibrant olive taste with full fruitiness. Gentle catch to the throat of pepperiness.
Safeway – £1.98 500ml/ £3.95 1 litre. Sweet and more characteristic of the French varities. Mellow with very little kick.
Sainsbury's – £2.29 250ml DU CANINO. The only single estate oil sold in supermarkets. Powerful with grassy flavour. Very strong with plenty of bite.
Tesco – £2.14 500ml/ £2.95 750ml. Earthy flavour marred by slight coarseness. Lots of bite and pepperiness.
Waitrose – £1.15 250ml/ £1.89 500ml/ £3.85 1 litre. Sweet and full bodied. Grassy with gentle pepperiness.

The increase of British interest in olive oil, now that it has made the journey from the chemist's counter to the supermarket shelves, has encouraged the importing of premium extra virgin and virgin estate oils from Italy and Spain. While these estate oils might just appeal to foodies and people with money to burn, their low acidity grading means that they may be the healthiest oils available. A brand new study from the Institut de Corps Gras in Paris has revealed that the anti-oxidants thought to be the most important contribution to the fight against heart disease, are only to be found in extra virgin and virgin olive oil rather than the blends. A high price for a healthy heart perhaps? Luckily no; there are plenty of extra virgin and virgin oils which come from a blend of olives from around the world and are easily affordable.

The Oil Merchant's Guide to Oils

Charles Carey has given us an idea of some of the more interesting – though not too cheap – estate oils available in Britain.

ITALIAN EXTRA VIRGIN OILS

Badia a Coltibuono – The Chianti classico estate was severely affected by the frosts in 1985 and so they now buy in some oil to complement their own production. They bottle an oil with a concentrated herbaceous flavour and a peppery aftertaste.

Colonna comes from the estate of Prince Colonna in the Molise region of central Italy. It is made from four varieties of hand-picked olives, blended to give a rich grassy flavour.

Dell 'Ugo – From the Florence/Sienna area, this oil is cloudy with some natural sediment. It is a vibrant green colour and has the powerful flavour and aroma of fresh olives.

Tenuta di Saragano – From the Umbrian hills above Todi, this oil comes from trees which are more than 400 years old. It is a light and elegant oil with very low acidity.

Tenuta Carparzo – produced and bottled in Tuscany, it is an intense green colour and has a grassy freshness with a low acidity.

Ravida – From Menfi near Sicily, it tastes of meadow hay with a delicate peppery aftertaste.

The die-hard foodie might want to try *Boscovivo* flavoured oils which are estate oils steeped with truffles and mushrooms. Use for flavouring rather than cooking. For example, dribble a few drops of the Porcini oil over a pasta salad, the truffle over Brassaola and slithers of Parmesan. Each bottle contains approximately 20 servings.

Granverde Colonna – Extra virgin oil with natural essence of lemons. These are new and unique oils made to a traditional family recipe of Prince Colonna. Hand-picked olives and untreated lemons from the estate are processed to make an oil with a strong citrus taste and aroma. Drizzle over fish, meat and cooked vegetables and salads. Do not use for cooking.

SPANISH OILS

Spanish oils tend to be lighter in style than the Italian oils; they do not have such a peppery aftertaste but have fruity or nutty flavours. The average Briton will recognize these oils – our palate likes the Spanish oils best and the products of Italy found in the supermarket will, for that reason, mostly be blends with a high proportion of Spanish oils.

Lerida – from the village of the same name near Barcelona. A light oil with a fresh nutty taste.

L'Estornell – from the same area. Certified organic by the Spanish government and the French group Nature et Progress. Virtually identical to Lerida.

FRENCH OILS

French farmhouses often do not have enough production to allow bottling of their oils under their own label; many go to cooperatives and others are sold to commercial concerns to blend with oils from other regions. In Provence and Languedoc, most of the oil is used for local consumption.

A L'Olivier is an extra virgin oil which comes from Nice and has a sweet olive fruitiness and little or none of that Italian pepperiness.

Le Vieux Moulin is also extra virgin and comes from a single variety of olive: the Tanche grown by M Farnoux in Mirabel in the Southern Rhône. He uses the family press which has been in the family for four generations and produces a sweet, fruity oil with a perfect balance.

Plagniol is a well-flavoured general-purpose olive oil for everyday use, and is especially good for mayonnaise.

GREEK OILS

These can be heavy and greasy, the product of olives that have been allowed to become overripe. Mani is one which emulates the Italian oils – it comes from the Peloponnese in Southern Greece and has a luscious yet fresh taste.

Olive oil has a lot in common with the history of wines in this country. Ten years ago the British knew very little about wines. There were fine wines and there was 'plonk'. The gap has closed these days, with supermarkets offering a huge selection of affordable interesting wines from all over the world which will not intimidate the average shopper. It is an easy comparison to make with olive oil. At the moment, Mr and Mrs Public are pulling faces at the idea of substituting it for cheap corn oil, commenting on the expense, the taste and the calories. The supermarkets offer around twenty brands of oil in their superstores throughout the country, but closer inspection would reveal a conservative array, with one oil tasting pretty much the same as the next. It is a low-risk commitment from the high street to olive oil, but it is as important a move as importing the mass of the dull, but clean and inexpensive, wines of the eighties. It is creating an awareness and a much more interesting future for the British palate.

Tastes and smells range from almond to apple, cucumber to earthy, while others recall freshly mown grass. The flavour of the estate oils is strong, and Charles Carey suggests using them in dressings or as a final touch to a dish. At a tasting at The Oil Merchant, we tried the Azienda Agricola Ravida from the southern coast of Sicily; this reminded us of bananas. Charles Carey suggests pouring this oil over salmon steaks before baking them in foil. At £14 per 75cl bottle, this is for the connoisseur or the convert.

Are these fine wines of olive oil so different to the blends, as their 1992 price of £15, £20, even £25 per litre (1¾ pints) would suggest? Judy Ridgway, author of the Mitchell Beazley *Pocket Guide To Oils, Vinegars and Seasonings*, reckons not. 'Estate oils are generally a special variety of olive, or a controlled blend. In the same way as the grand marque champagnes, the estates stick to a very distinct recipe. It takes a lot of time and money to make them, so they become very expensive to buy. That's not to say though that the cheaper blends are any worse, and as people in this country become more aware of what they like in their olive oil, they're going to be less intimidated by the connoisseurs and the high prices than the wine buyers were in the eighties.'

While the north of Italy's supplies dwindle, the southern abundance of olives is beginning to hit headlines in response to the growing requests for oil by supermarkets all over the world. Puglia, Basilicata and Calabria, with a population of six million to fill the heel of Italy, produce ten per cent of the country's total olive production. The local cuisine is based on the land's natural goodies – grain, grapes and olives. Bread is big in Puglia, with many unusual types on sale. Here the locals dip their bread into the olive oil in the same way as we put butter on a roll when eating out.

Southern Italian estate oil producers, Damiana and Gianni Calogiuri, are the current managers of a family firm which has been growing olives in Puglia since 1825. They are aware that the Tuscan PR machine has been keen to cover over the fact that there simply might not be enough local olives to go around in the North. It might seem that the Calogiuris have been slow to make the most of their quantity as well as the quality of their Southern olives, but they are making up for lost time. Their groves in the countryside around Lecce produce more olives than they know what to do with. As well as producing a range of oils from their 200-year-old trees and flavoured with basil, garlic, rosemary and oregano, which should just now have reached British supermarkets, they also use their extra virgin oil to produce biscuits. Baked in fires fuelled by olive branches, and sweetened with almonds, the dessert Falanita cookies which gastronomes will dip in sweet wines, and which biscuit fans will devour as a legitimate part of the Mediterranean Diet could be just what the doctor ordered. They are due to arrive in this country soon with accompanying savoury biscuits for cheese or snacks. Environmentally friendly and free of animal fats, this will be a valuable help in steering us away from the hidden sugars and fats in our traditional biscuits.

Baking biscuits with olive oil is something which virgin users will not have imagined trying. But Judy Ridgway believes that shoppers will ultimately become so aware of the different oils, that they will use one for deep frying, others for salads and condiments and the wider range for an endless number of recipes. All this sounds extremely expensive however, and brings us to the three main problems the average shopper will raise when told about the health benefits of olive oil:

1. it's too expensive
2. it's got a funny taste and
3. it's fattening.

Ridgway puts this down to typical British reserve about new products. 'Using less oil for cooking means that price for price, olive oil is no more expensive, and it's perfectly possible to use it for all types of cooking. The fact that you actually taste the oil you're cooking in is something we're not used to in this country', she says. 'Rapeseed doesn't have any flavour, and that's quite a deliberate move by its manufacturers. But we *are* used to a buttery taste, so it's just a matter of making the leap in our perception of fats having flavour. It might also be worrying for some people that it's so visible. Most of the food we eat absorbs the oil it's cooked in so it doesn't appear to be swimming in grease. Once people realize that olive oil is good for us, it won't be such a problem. As far as calories are concerned, it's a complete myth that olive oil has more. All oils have the same calorific value.'

Ironically, the more aware Britain becomes of the

benefits of the Mediterranean Diet, the more the young Southern Europeans are becoming Flora men and women. In parts of Spain and Greece, olive oil is dismissed as granny food and already, manufactured foods, high in the sort of saturated fats we're being weaned off in this country, are promoting a rise in heart disease in the Mediterranean.

As the British reserve begins to break down, the olive oil industry grows. The future means that the indolent harvesting will have to move into a different gear; estate growers may find consortiums a lucrative means of marketing what each of them may have in short supply; and we may even find new groves developing in other sunny climes. Turkey, Portugal, Israel, Iraq, Iran, Albania, the former Yugoslavia, South Africa, Jordan and Syria are among the countries growing olives. If California and Australia can compete with French fine wines, there's little reason why we shouldn't see their olive groves producing fine oils there too. With heart attacks on the rise in both countries, perhaps the little olive can do more for world health than any study, doctor or government could ever hope to achieve.

CHAPTER 4

Message in a Bottle

Our English-speaking cousins across the pond cannot be accused of contributing much to the world of haute cuisine, although we do have the tomato to thank them for – the basis of so much Mediterranean cooking. But they also gave birth to the fast food monster and, at the same time, created a nation so obsessed with self-image that, for many, dieting is a career.

On the bright side, though, the USA is a country where *good* ideas catch on too, and towards the end of 1991 something happened which set the public imagination alight and turned a piece of academic research into a commercial success story, virtually overnight.

All over the United States, liquor stores and supermarkets suddenly started to report a huge upsurge in sales of red wine – unheard of in a nation of beer and Bourbon drinkers. Millions of people – from young men to little old ladies – were buying red wine like it was going out of fashion, not for snob value but for health.

The catalyst for this remarkable turnabout was a television programme. CBS's *60 Minutes*, transmitted on 17 November 1991, explored reasons why the French smoke more, exercise less and eat more fat, yet suffer significantly fewer heart attacks than the Americans. (As in Britain, CHD is the USA's number one killer.)

The programme, called 'The French Paradox', centred around work carried out by two leading researchers in heart disease – Dr Curtis Ellison of the Boston University School of Medicine and Dr Serge Renaud whose work with heart attack victims was described in the previous chapter. What drew the Americans attention was Renaud's conclusion that a consumption of alcohol, particularly wine, could reduce the risk of heart disease by at least forty per cent. It was music to the ears of the twenty-two million households who tuned in that night. They latched on to red wine being a life-saver since the French drink so much of it and, as a result, supermarket red wine sales surged by forty-four per cent in the four-week period following the broadcast.

Renaud explained that the situation in France is paradoxical in that, although the French eat a good deal of saturated fat in their diet, they have very little coronary heart disease. 'This paradox may be attributable, in part, to high wine consumption,' he indicated, pointing out that the opposite of the French paradox can be found in Britain. He puts this down to our comparatively low consumption of wine.

There have been other studies, however, showing that people who drink *any* alcohol in moderation live longer than teetotallers or heavy drinkers because alcohol can raise HDL – high density lipo-proteins.

What sets Renaud's study apart though, is his emphasis on wine. 'Because wine is mostly consumed during meals, it is absorbed slowly, and thus has a prolonged protective effect.' The protective effect, Renaud suggests, is on blood which, during meal times, is particularly 'under the influence' of lipids or fats. Since the French drink mostly red wine at mealtimes, the answer could be in the skin, which is not included in white wine. The skin of red grapes contains anti-oxidants which protect against heart disease. Or it may be something in the tannin.

Meanwhile, wine should be the preferred alcoholic choice anyway since it is a vital component of the healthy Mediterranean diet and is associated with mealtimes as opposed to drinking for drinking's sake. That, if nothing else, puts it ahead.

The search to find a connection between wine and health is not new. In his book *Vin et Santé*, published in 1960, Dr Jean Max Eylaud lists a whole host of human ills which could benefit from drinking wine. He suggests that wine is one of the oldest natural cures, along with 'taking the waters', mud baths, herbal infusions and good mountain air. 'The first doctor, Aesculapius, used all these natural phenomena to cure illnesses. Therefore it comes as little surprise that the vine grapes and their fermented juice have entered the arsenal of healers of all types and of all names throughout the ages.'

WHAT IS 'MODERATE' DRINKING?

In his study, Serge Renaud stresses the importance of drinking wine in moderate amounts to prevent cirrhosis of the liver and plain drunkenness.

The British idea of moderate drinking, however, is not quite the same as the Mediterraneans. In Crete, for instance, they drink between two and three glasses of wine every day and their life expectancy is one of the greatest in the world. And two-three glasses a day is what Serge Renaud recommends, stressing that the most enjoyment and the greatest health benefit comes from drinking wine with food.

Wine Units

1 unit = 1 standard glass = one sixth of a bottle

The Health Education Authority (HEA) advises slightly less than does Serge Renaud. Its advice is that women should drink no more than fourteen glasses (units) a week, and men no more than twenty-one. So, for a woman to drink more than two glasses a day would mean being over the HEA's limit. It also recommends drink-free days in between, as if we should punish ourselves for having enjoyed something. This further fuels the wrath of the bon viveurs, already raging about Britain's 'food terrorists'. The real key to healthy drinking is to drink with food, something the Mediterraneans do instinctively.

Wine-drinking League

Per head consumption of wine drunk in Britain puts us at the bottom of the league table.

1990

France – 74 litres = 98 bottles
Italy – 62 litres = 82 bottles
Portugal – 48 litres = 64 bottles
Spain – 38 litres = 51 bottles
Britain – 12 litres = 16 bottles

The British, as everyone knows, prefer beer. In 1990 the average British beer drinker managed to put away 135.7 litres (237.5 pints).

EAT, DRINK AND BE MEDITERRANEAN

It's a far cry from the macho male in the British pub, jangling his change in a ritual swagger to the bar to buy the next round, to the laid-back café society of the Mediterranean where wine and chat are treated with equal priority. There, drinking is not just social, it's a way of life.

In Greece, drink is extremely familiar but drunkenness almost unknown. It's the European home of the vine, and being drunk is not only unusual but totally unacceptable. Very few places exist simply to sell alcohol in Greece. The taverna is the equivalent, not of a pub but of a restaurant, and Greeks regard 'bars' as specially contrived to cater for foreign tourists.

In Italy, drunks are regarded as wimps. Anyone who doesn't understand how to handle an everyday and unremarkable substance is a fool. At the table, wine is as natural as breaking bread.

The same is true of France. The French love eating and they know that their food tastes even better with wine than without. And in which other country would you find a marathon route punctuated with medically approved 'wine stops', as in the Bordeaux marathons of 1986 and 1987?

BOTTOMS UP

We need only remember a typical British phrase when raising a glass with a drinking partner to realize how different we are from the Mediterraneans in our attitude to drink. Here, the idea seems to be that getting drunk is the best possible way to enjoy it. 'Bottoms up!' implies 'Let's get rid of it fast, so that we can see the bottom of the glass.' 'Cheers' is preferable. The French, meanwhile, toast health – 'Santé!' – and they mean it.

Don Hewitson, a New Zealander who came to Britain twenty years ago to open a wine bar, finds the average British drinker has the same psyche as his fellow countrymen. 'When I came here, I found a drinking culture practically the same as back home. The idea of a good night out was getting drunk and having a curry, and it's still pretty much the same. That's not the way to enjoy food, and it's certainly not the way to enjoy wine. Too many British still treat wine like beer – cheap and cheerful "wallop" to be consumed as fast as possible. There's no thought that perhaps one good bottle of wine might be better than three bottles of plonk.'

Don thinks that the best way to make sure that we don't breed a new generation of hooligans who see alcohol as a means to oblivion, is to bring children up to regard drinking as a part of life. That means letting children sit down to meals where wine is drunk. Don's slogan is 'Drink less when you're not eating'. As he raises his glass, he says that if he doesn't die of hardening of the arteries, he will be the first son in five generations to avoid this and the first to drink red wine. So far, so good.

LOTTA BOTTLE

Even though we drink less wine per head than other European countries, our intake has climbed steadily over the years. We now drink three times the amount we did in 1971. In this country, wine used to be like opera – a prerogative of the élite and designed to baffle. But thanks to the supermarkets, which moved into the wine market in a big way in the early seventies, wine has gradually been demystified. Own labels and clearer information mean that we now know more about what we're buying and no longer have to turn away in ignorance.

Sainsbury's paved the way with the sweetness indicator – on a level of 1–9, 1 being the dryest and 9 the sweetest – and other supermarkets followed suit. High-street outlets have also been instrumental in removing wine snobbery, like the multiple Oddbins whose staff are trained to answer any queries about wine. And if the huge range in the off-licence still puts you off, there's always the wine box which doesn't have the class implications of the traditional bottle and reduces wine to the status of just another drink – like orange juice or milk.

Gill Reynolds, who owns The Hermitage wine shop in north London, says people shouldn't be afraid to ask for advice. 'I can then ask *them* questions. What taste do they like? Dry, medium or sweet? How much do they want to spend? What do they want it for – everyday drinking or a special occasion? Who's going to be drinking it with them? For instance, older people prefer sweeter wines. Once

I've got answers to all these questions, I can then go for the country of origin. Generally speaking, the hotter the country, the heavier the wine.'

France, Spain and Italy may produce their own wines, catapulting them to the top of the wine-drinking league, but we have a wider variety of wines to choose from than any other European country.

Food and wine critic Nigel Barden suggests that Britain is one of the most coveted markets for the international wine producer. 'The number and variety of wines available in this country are unequalled anywhere in Europe,' he says. 'Most of the wine-producing regions in other countries only sell their own product. Try asking for a Rioja in Bordeaux, and you'll probably be kicked out of the restaurant. But with retail outlets like Oddbins offering wines from the New World, Chile and Spain as well as the more established wines from France and Italy, the British wine buyer can afford to be more discriminating. It knocks on the head the old myth that we don't know anything about wines. We actually know much more than we think, and wine producers are always trying to get their product into Britain.'

So there's no excuse. That cold bottle of Retsina you sipped slowly on a Greek island in the evening sun, the crisp fragrant rosé which coursed through your body on a Provençal picnic, or the light Chianti you quaffed whilst toasting the Tuscan countryside sometime last summer, need no longer be just a holiday romance.

An average glass of wine = about 95 calories

WINE OF THE GODS

Wine's been around a long time. It's mentioned no fewer than 150 times in the Old Testament and ten in the New

Testament and in ancient mythology Dionysus in Greece and Bacchus in Rome were the gods of wine. Its place in religion is confirmed. In ancient Mediterranean cultures, wine was the most popular gift to be offered up to the gods.

Stone Age man cultivated the vine, perhaps as early as 8000 BC in what was then Transcaucasia, between the Black Sea and the Caspian Sea. The vine really took hold in the southern half of what is now Italy around 200 BC and it was the Romans who were responsible for transporting it across Europe, including Britain. We still have 2,500 acres, but our own wine is an acquired taste. By the way, don't get confused between British wine and English wine. British wine is made from imported grape must – unfermented grape juice – and it's pretty filthy stuff. English wine, on the other hand, has, by law, to be made from imported vines cultured in Britain and it's mostly the German grape varieties which do well here.

Testimony

PHILIP OWENS
Chef

Philip Owens is the 33-year-old chef whose recipes make up a large proportion of the dishes in the second half of this book. Six years ago he was virtually crippled with arthritis. The pains in his legs were due to avascular nucrosis, which stops the blood supply reaching the hip. As the bone started to die off, the pain became unbearable and he cut out all dairy products, switched to Mediterranean-style foods and avoided a combination of protein and carbohydrate foods in the same meal.

He lost a stone (6.35 kg) in six months, and now, two years later, has his weight down from 12½ stone (79.5 kg) to 10 stone (63.5 kg). His restaurant – the Arts Theatre Café in central London – serves the rustic, peasant food which is the

Mediterranean Diet at its best.

'I didn't really consider it to be a diet in the old sense of the word. It was certainly no hardship, and the arthritis has completely gone.'

WINE WITH FOOD

When matching wine with food, remember that there aren't many combinations which can be dismissed outright as 'wrong', but generations of experience have produced certain conventions.

The general rule is to serve white wine with delicate flavours and red wine with strong, meaty flavours. Don Hewitson suggests that you don't have to stick rigidly to this. 'I've never considered chicken and white wine a match made in heaven. I always prefer a lightish, red Burgundy. And a flavoursome fish grilled with a prominent herb seasoning will go perfectly with a light young red.'

The latest trend is to serve red wine slightly colder than usual because wine lovers have realized that when the term 'room temperature' was first conceived as a rule of thumb for red wines, the rooms were considerably cooler than nowadays. In France there is now a fashion to cook fish with red wine – untraditional partners. Alain Reymond of the Auberge de Saint-Hilaire in the Nîmes area of Languedoc, cooks monkfish with red wine because he finds this fish slightly characterless. 'The tannin in the red wine gives this dish an excellent flavour. Red wine also works well with river fish, like trout.' It's all a matter of taste.

In a restaurant, you really don't have to insist on Burgundy with venison or know what château bottling means to order and enjoy wine. Not many people can actually spot the difference between great and merely good vintages.

Nigel Barden's Wine Tips

A cold rosé is excellent with light lunches on a hot summer day.

A red will taste at its best when warmed from cold to room temperature.

Avoid citrus fruits with wine.

Vinegar doesn't go well with wine, so dress salads with a splash of vinegar and a higher proportion of good quality olive oil.

Store wine on its side in a cool place.

Good quality wines benefit from the bottle standing upright for half an hour before pouring.

Nibble a little plain bread before tasting.

Where you would automatically go for a red to cut through the flavour of a heavy meat, try a white from the Rhône Valley. They're unusually solid and dense wines. When blindfolded and offered one of these, many tasters have been unable to tell them from a red.

Try the same wine in six different glasses to see the difference the surface area in the glass can make to the taste. A champagne will lose all its bubbles in anything other than a flute, while a red in a large Burgundy glass will benefit greatly from the contact with the air.

Never fill a red wine glass more than one-third full. The wine must be allowed to breathe.

A red wine, in particular, has an ever-changing character. It will change while it's in the bottle too, so be sure to lay it down properly if you want to keep it for a special occasion.

If a cork is allowed to dry out by storing the bottle upright, it will shrink and let the air in. The wine will be 'corked' when you open it. This means that it will be tainted by the taste of the dried cork.

If the wine has a lead neck capsule, make sure you cut it at least 1mm below the top of the bottle to avoid the wine being poured over the lead and spoiling the taste. Surprisingly large amounts of lead can be picked up this way.

If you don't finish your bottle in one sitting, it won't taste the same the next time. Even though you may have put the cork back in, the air will have begun the oxidization process, thereby losing its initial freshness.

Most red wines taste better from a decanter because they will have been given a greater opportunity to breathe. Too much exposure to the air, though, will make the wine go off, so our advice is to drink it with friends and finish the bottle.

Port should be drunk from a decanter. You can keep it, but it will lose its fruity taste.

The reason red wines are decanted is to sift out the sediment. A red wine like Beaujolais Nouveau can develop a sediment in a very short time because it is designed to be drunk immediately. Conversely, wines that have aged in the bottle over years develop a sediment much more slowly as part of the maturing process of a full-bodied wine.

A crystal can form in some white wines. This is called tartrate and is quite normal, particularly in sweeter wines. Some people camplain because it looks as though sugar has been added, but this is a sign of quality.

Wine Guide

Specific wines have been suggested to accompany the recipes in the second half of this book, but here is a generic guide:

Food	*Wine*
Shellfish	Dry white, or sparkling, champagne. An unusual contrast is sherry or dessert wine
Fish	Dry white, dry rosé, light red, or sparkling, champagne

Oily fish	**Dry white, or fresh zesty red**
Dried meat	**Dry white, dry rosé, semi-sweet rosé, or light red**
White meat	**Dry white, dry rosé, light red, or sparkling, champagne**
Red meat	**Light red, or full-bodied red. Alternatively, try a full white from the Rhône valley.**
Game birds	**Light red, or full-bodied red**
Game meat	**Full-bodied red**
Dessert	**Semi-sweet rosé, or sweet white**

CHAPTER 5

Cupboard Love

Now that you know what the Mediterranean Diet means, you need to find out something about the individual foods which are central to it so that you can make the right choices. You also need to know what to eat less of, bearing in mind that the Diet is not about *totally* giving up favourite indulgencies but about giving priority to certain foods which will bring you maximum health as well as put you at your optimum weight.

The debris in your pedal bin should not be full of discarded packets and wrappings from processed food, but the few inedible bits of the *real* food you'll prepare as part of your new diet. The less rubbish you put out for the 'vulture' truck, the less you'll be putting in your body.

Once you cut down on the saturated fatty foods, you'll leave more room for potatoes, bread, pasta and cereals, like rice. Contrary to popular belief, these are not the culprits in the weight war; it's the butter, sugar, full-fat milk and creamy sauces you put on them which are to blame. And when you've weaned your body off the artificial 'high' you get from a eating a sugary cream bun, you'll develop a new appetite for the fish, fruit, vegetables and pulses which are the other key constituents of the Mediterranean Health Diet.

Sugar and fat are unhealthy sources of energy, so your body needs a healthy substitute. Starchy carbohydrates, like bread, potatoes, pasta and rice provide this and, like fruit and vegetables, they are also excellent sources of dietary fibre. And fruit and vegetables are full of anti-oxidants.

Anti-Oxidants

'Anti-oxidant' is the new buzz word and one of the most important constituents of the Mediterranean Health Diet.

Anti-oxidants ward off the free radicals which are a natural result of the oxygen-using processes in our bodies.

Free radicals are also formed as a reaction to smoking, car exhausts and other pollution.

Left to their own devices, free radicals can form a chain reaction which can cause serious damage to cells and possibly contribute to heart disease and cancer.

Anti-oxidants in Vitamin C, beta-carotene, Vitamin E and some minerals all fight off free radicals and can be found widely in fruit and vegetables.

Anti-oxidants are affected by the way we treat fruit and vegetables. The fresher, the better.

Fish and vegetable oils also contain anti-oxidants.

Pre-preparation of fruit and vegetables by supermarkets and in the home reduces Vitamin C and beta-carotene levels within 30 minutes.

Orange juice is a good provider of Vitamin C when freshly squeezed or freshly opened, but levels decline within hours of display in light, or life on a kitchen-shelf.

Buy fruit and vegetables fresh and eat them quickly.

Leave vegetable preparation until last.

Cook vegetables in a minimum amount of water, for a minimum amount of time and serve immediately.

These foods will not only get your body to work better for you, they'll also fill you up because they provide bulk. So, you'll be more likely to keep the weight off. And once you've incorporated fish – which is an excellent source of protein – olive oil, herbs and wine, not to mention all the extra vitamins and minerals you'll get from your new diet, you'll look and feel so healthy you'll wonder why you stuck to your old ways for so long.

HOW DIETARY FIBRE WORKS IN THE BODY

So, starchy carbohydrates provide energy, but what is dietary fibre? Simply, it's the indigestible part of plant foods like fruit, vegetables, pulses and cereals which helps get rid of the waste that's left after you've digested your food by sweeping it through your body.

Fibre has little nutritional value, but the bulk it provides stimulates the muscular wall of the large intestine. The waste products can then move along quickly and pass out, almost unchanged, regularly and without strain. No more rabbit droppings and no more constipation.

Passing waste through quickly like this helps remove the harmful substances your body makes before they can increase the risk of diseases, like bowel cancer. And fibre is entirely non-fattening.

Vitamins and Minerals

Vitamins = micronutrients which promote health.

Minerals = nutrients essential for health and the growth of teeth and bones.

The Mediterranean Health Diet contains all you need in the way of vitamins and minerals, so you don't need supplements.

PASTA

Pasta means paste in Italian and is based on starchy dough. As Maddalena Bonino of London's Bertorelli's restaurant puts it, 'Of all the starch which is the pillar of

Italian cuisine, pasta is the most versatile.'

There are two kinds of dough – one with egg and one without. Eggless pasta is made from a variety of flours, including wholemeal and rice flour. Dried, commercial pasta is the most familiar type of eggless pasta and is made with hard wheat (durum) flour and water, making a resilient dough to withstand rolling and shaping by machine. Dried, eggless pasta has an indefinite shelf-life and comes in countless shapes and sizes.

Maddalena prefers cooking with dried pasta 'because it holds the flavour of sauces so well. In Britain, there's a snob value attached to fresh pasta, but a good plate of pasta is a good plate of pasta. It's the way you cook it.'

Dried pasta should be cooked *al dente*' (firm to the teeth). Fresh pasta – which you can buy or make yourself, if you have a pasta machine and the patience – takes only a few seconds to cook in boiling water. Dried pasta takes anything from five minutes for tagliatelli, to fifteen to twenty minutes for shaped pasta.

Maddalena finds dried pasta a good way of winning children over. 'Kids love the different shapes, and it's so easy to digest. I like to cook it in a chicken or vegetable broth. Pasta only becomes fattening depending on the sauce you add.' For a good healthy meal in a hurry, Maddalena suggests heating whole cloves of garlic in olive oil, adding freshly cut chillies and then removing the chillies and garlic just before adding cooked spaghetti. 'You get different levels of flavour from the garlic and hotness from the chillies depending on how long you leave them in.' Another of Maddalena's suggestions is chopped, skinned tomatoes cut up in lemon juice and extra virgin olive oil. 'When you put in the hot spaghetti, it has a marinating effect. It's a beautiful smell – you're actually eating the smell. Both these dishes are best with dried pasta.'

Maddalena stresses that the secret to a successful pasta sauce is not to mix too many ingredients together. 'Just concentrate on one or two flavours – don't turn it into a stir-fry.'

In Maddalena's view, the British don't really consider pasta as a main dish. 'They think of it as an accompaniment. You'd be surprised how many people who eat at my restaurant want to order spaghetti bolognese as a side dish to meat.'

POTATOES

Potatoes divide into two types – waxy and mealy. The firm, waxy type has a high moisture content, with low starch and a thin skin. These are best for boiling because they don't fall apart so easily. A mealy or floury potato has more starch. It's light and fluffy when you cook it and best for baking and puréeing.

In Britain, the most widely available, all-purpose potato is the white King Edward. A lot of the fibre in potatoes is in its skin, or just below it.

BREAD

It's not for nothing that bread is called 'the staff of life'. No food has as much history as the harvesting of grain, the milling of flour, the fermentation of dough and the raising of bread.

There are two types of breads: those made with yeast and those without. Brown bread is richer in fibre and vitamins than white bread and some breads have extra wheatgerm or bran added to them, giving them an even higher fibre content. Wholewheat bread is made from the wholewheat kernel, making it rich in vitamins and high in fibre.

Maddalena Bonino says, 'You don't really need to put anything on your bread if it's nice. You have to re-educate your palate to do without butter and spreads. It's all a question of learning from another culture. In Italy, bread is a matter of pride. You can go into any village and find a great selection of bread. With our tradition of sauces, many people use bread to mop up. That's something the British should learn. And our sandwiches are a very different experience. The "tramezzini" is almost a meal in itself.'

One of Maddalena's tips is Ciabatta bread with marinated olives, and no butter. 'It's a poor man's snack and it's completely delicious.'

RICE

Rice comes in a variety of shapes, sizes and colours. Short-grain rice has more starch than medium or long-grain and is a perfect choice for Italian risottos.

'Risotto rice should be cooked *al dente*, like pasta,' says Maddalena. 'The easiest to buy is Arborio rice. Risotto is very fluffy so you shouldn't expect to eat a lot of it. You can have it with anything – fish, meat, vegetables, asparagus, fresh clams, mussels, squid, frogs' legs or just fresh peas. You can add these at any time while you're cooking. It could be just a matter of perfuming it, or you can be as inventive as you like. Good risotto is a technique. You try to get the rice to absorb the water and release the starch. It should be stirred for the twenty minutes it takes to cook, to stop it sticking. A wide shallow pan, like a casserole dish, is best, and don't put it on a high heat.'

Testimony

PATRICIA

Patricia is a diabetic of fifty-seven. A year ago, she was 15 stone (95.25 kg) and suffering from arthritis. Her doctor decided to take her off painkillers and send her to the dietitian to see if she could lose the weight and change her eating habits.

She had been working as a warden for the elderly and not eating through five-hour shifts. Suddenly finding the desperate need for food that diabetics suffer in order to boost their blood sugar level, she would cram in anything that was available. A grandmother of fifteen, she was used to having children and their accompanying biscuits and sweets around her all the time.

Patricia's dietitian encouraged her to try the Mediterranean Diet and to plan her daily eating routine. She was told that five small meals a day were much better than a chocolate bar every couple of hours. She was not to try to lose more than 1½ lb (0.68 kg) per week so that she would keep the weight off. After one year, she's down to 11½ stone (73 kg). She loves the fresher, tastier food and feels that she has much more energy than she's ever had. She's off the painkillers for her arthritis and doesn't miss them at all.

VEGETABLES

Just a few generations ago, the seasons strictly defined which vegetables were available. Today's huge variety is the result of modern cultivation, genetic engineering and better transportation. Supermarkets now sell a wide range, but flavour is often sacrificed for shiny uniformity.

At the peak of their season, fresh vegetables come to life with just the minimum of seasoning, perhaps just a little salt and pepper, a dash of lemon juice or a sprinkling of herbs. As well as wonderful alone or in combination, some vegetables, like onions and tomatoes, become an integral part of the flavour of certain dishes in the Mediterranean Diet. They're naturally high in vitamins and nutrients, contain little fat and no cholesterol.

Philip Owens of the Arts Theatre Café in London, uses more vegetables than meat in his cooking. To him, they're a meal, not just a supplement. 'Some of my best dishes come from eating what's to hand. Stick to vegetables which are seasonal. Hot-house peppers and tomatoes have no flavour. Serve vegetables the Italian way – as a dish on their own – and treat them with respect. The more the merrier is not the answer. You're better off doing one really well. I steam my vegetables and serve a lot raw. Carrots dressed with orange juice, pine nuts and extra virgin olive oil are great. I also grill a lot of vegetables on a cast-iron griddle and then marinate them in extra virgin olive oil and fresh herbs. This works well for aubergine, courgettes, chicory, asparagus and radiccio. Never, never over-boil vegetables.'

Philip is critical of the way the British think of salads. 'People think of salad as rabbit food and that's because they can only stretch their imagination to lettuce, cucumber and tomato. Make sure you do a good dressing – all you need is balsamic vinegar, extra-virgin olive oil and salt.'

PULSES

Pulses are plants with edible seeds in a pod, and include peas, beans, lentils, chick-peas and broad beans. Most dried pulses have to be soaked in water before cooking as this shortens cooking time and helps prevent splitting. They're likely to double in volume, so use a big pot. Ginger mixed in with pulses avoids wind. More importantly, cooking removes toxins from many pulses. Be particularly careful to soak and boil red kidney beans and chick-peas before eating.

FRUIT

Like vegetables, most fruit is available all year round but again, taste is often sacrificed for aesthetic beauty in the supermarket. Eat fruit as fresh as possible in order to benefit from the vitamins and valuable anti-oxidants.

Philip Owens recommends unexpected combinations like fennel and orange salad: 'It's very cleansing. I also like grilled oranges with smoked duck.'

HERBS

Herbs are now so widely available that only a few are restricted to a single country or area. The taste of any herb is most characteristic when it's uncooked. Fragile herbs like parsley and tarragon should be added towards the end of cooking. More robust herbs, such as thyme and rosemary, are best cooked for longer as their flavours infuse a dish more slowly. For flavour, herbs grown outdoors are best. Dried herbs have a much stronger flavour, so the quantity used should be less than for fresh herbs.

'Martino' Costanzo Martinucci of San Martino restaurant in London, cooks with herbs so much that he has his own herb garden at the back. 'I make a lot of clear broth from chicken and mixed bones and these go really well with various herbs. My kitchen is a real Italian kitchen – a *cucina naturale* – herbs everywhere.'

FISH

The two most important things about fish are how old it is and how well it's been kept. A good-quality fresh fish will be bright-eyed, still have its own sheen and the flesh will be firm, not flabby.

The taste of fish varies widely. Oily fish, like mackerel and herring, are as different from white-fleshed fish such as hake, as duck is from chicken. Texture is also important. For instance, the coarse flesh of cod is completely different from the fine texture of sole.

White fish is low in fat and high in vitamins and minerals; oily fish is rich in essential polyunsaturates.

After the war, there were 10,000 fishmongers in Britain; now there are only 2,000. Supermarkets have tried to make up the shortfall with wet fish counters but, increasingly, people buy fish filleted and packaged.

Michael Lear, of the fishmonger Chalmers and Gray in London, says, 'It's as if we have fish phobia in this country. Most people think that cooking fish is difficult, and it isn't. The secret is, it doesn't need much cooking. Since most fish can be eaten raw, the golden rule is don't overcook it or you'll dry out the oils and it'll end up like cardboard. The great thing about fish is, not only is there more variety than meat, but you can use all of it. Once you've eaten the flesh, you can make a stock out of the bones. And if you buy prawns in their shells instead of peeled, it's not only cheaper but you can use the shells for a sauce. A good tip is to fill an ice cube tray with fish stock made from prawn shells, and drop it in a prawn curry for flavour.'

Michael is amazed at the ignorance there is about fish. 'Some people don't know that a kipper is a smoked herring.'

Protein

Protein = large, complex molecules essential for structure, growth and repair of tissues.

MEAT AND POULTRY

Meat is not a major component of the Mediterranean Diet, although spicy sausages do feature. A favourite light lunch is salami with a little extra virgin olive oil and vegetables.

The visible fat should always be cut off meat because of its high saturated fat content. A small piece can be used to flavour a basic stew of pulses and meat as long as it is removed before eating.

Most of the fat in poultry, like chicken, is in the skin, so this needs to be removed.

Meat products, such as pies, sausages and salami are high in saturated fat which can't be removed, so keep them as an occasional treat.

DAIRY PRODUCTS

Since dairy products such as full-fat milk, cheese, butter and eggs are high in saturated fat, they should be limited.

Before 1983, only about four per cent of people drank semi-skimmed milk. Now it's more like forty per cent.

Sugar

Sugar provides energy, but no nutrients and it causes tooth decay. It's also fattening.

Salt

Salt should just be added for taste, not tipped on freely. Taste it, don't salt it.

High salt intake is related to high blood pressure. Replace some of the salt with herbs and spices for a healthier and tastier alternative.

Maddalena Bonino: 'You don't need a lot of expertise or time to use the foods in the Mediterranean Diet to their best advantage. If you care about what you put in your body, everything will follow naturally. Food shouldn't be processed pulp; we have teeth. Let children watch you cooking, feed them well and they'll be hooked for life.'

CHAPTER 6

Picking Your Way through the Menu

If you're on a diet, the last thing you generally want to do is go out to eat. The will-power probably just does not stretch that far, and to watch your nearest and dearest tuck into a chicken kiev while you suck a mange-tout, would more than likely drive you to a binge before bedtime.

Diets in the past have always been associated with restraint and have always, therefore, meant limiting the opportunities to go out to eat. Eating at home meant that you could weigh each potato and count every pea and be sure that you were on target for that pound a week weight loss. The Mediterranean Health Diet, on the other hand, actively encourages you to eat out. Sitting around the table with a group of friends or family, eating a really good meal, is going to do more to change your perception of food than any calorie counter will.

While restaurants on the Continent cater more for the casual eater, in Britain they tend to be associated with treats, and rich creamy food. But there is a growing band of young chefs who are incorporating lighter, more nutritiously balanced dishes in their menus, and encouraging others to follow their example. In the eighties, Nouvelle Cuisine was designed to leave expense account lunchers feeling less than weighed down, but it really only served to create hunger pangs by early afternoon. The lunch-as-objet idea soon translated into heartier portions, and prices soared accordingly.

With nutritionists and Government experts pushing the

need for Britain to rethink its eating habits, the opportunity to lead the revolution was handed to the chefs on a plate. Not necessarily the most health-conscious people, they nonetheless have inspired a generation of foodies and cooks to be more imaginative with food. As a result, not only are we overturning the popular foreign perception of British food as being little more than grease on newspaper, but British chefs are earning an international reputation for the first time in decades.

Haute cuisine is like haute couture; the fashion designers who parade their whacky ideas on the world stage actively encourage imitation. They set the trends and within a couple of months, their creations are available in the high street for a fraction of the cost. True, the courgettes en fleur which you'll find at Raymond Blanc's Le Manoir aux Quat' Saisons might not make it to the kitchens of the Happy Eater, but a version of his roast fillet of monkfish served with mustard and tarragon sauce may well be on the menu at a restaurant near you. With so many top chefs publishing their recipes these days, it would be an arrogant or insular chef who did not take a leaf out of their copybooks.

The Guide to Eating Out

Look through the menu before you choose to eat at a restaurant, and see how many creamy sauces there are. It's a poor chef who can't think beyond a carton of whipping cream.

Try to pick a dish without dairy products. Pasta dishes with a tomato base are much better for you. Grilled meats and fish are likely to retain more of their own flavour if they are not drowned in a sauce.

Vegetable dishes are catching on all over the country and can often be more imaginative than a steak au poivre. A chef who can't think about what to do with a few

vegetables probably isn't worth his salt.

If you can, choose a restaurant where the chef is known to be a bit creative – he or she is more likely to be able to think laterally about healthy eating and won't palm you off with a veggie burger.

The research for this book took us to many great restaurants where we met chefs who are meeting the challenge for a healthier diet. There were also those who are reluctant to have restrictions placed upon them, such as doing without dairy products or animal fats, but when the most outraged of them had finished their diatribe on food terrorism, we noticed that their menus had a wide variety of mouthwatering dishes which unintentionally follow the guidelines of the Mediterranean Health Diet. Many of them are featured in the second part of this book.

Many restaurants are also actually taking a pro-active stance in setting trends for better eating habits. Antony Worrall Thompson, chef at 190 Queensgate, and the recently opened dell'Ugo in London's Soho told us that the Mediterranean Diet is not just another trend. 'Nouvelle Cuisine was a fashion,' he said, 'something hungry men put up with in the eighties because it was chic to eat nasturtiums. But it wasn't necessarily much healthier – many of the sauces were cream-based – you just didn't get much of it, and felt that you'd done your body a favour by leaving it half empty. The more Mediterranean-style food is not only better for you, you don't leave feeling absolutely ravenous. I think it's more a man's food – it's hearty and filling, but appeals to women too because they tend to be more conscious of what they eat. It can also be much cheaper than many traditional haute cuisine dishes.' Worrall Thompson prepares snacks at dell'Ugo which for £4 each (1992) will fill the hungriest stomachs.

Getting More from Your Menu

Simply asking your waiters about your food means that you'll be encouraging them to write a menu which will be more informative next time. A restaurant which has taken the peasant diet of the Mediterranean and turned it into food fit for London's notorious gastro-snobs, is Soho Soho. Much of its menu is an inventive rewording of the World Health Organization (WHO) nutritional guidelines. Each dish is described so that the customer knows exactly how the dish is made. Increasing numbers of restaurants are doing this, mainly to tantalize the taste-buds, but also to encourage a better knowledge about food. Tony Howarth, chef at Soho Soho, has contributed a number of excellent recipes to the second half of this book (see pages 223-9).

Soho Soho's description of its food might be clearer than most, but customers may also want to raise certain questions about the nature of the oil, or the ingredients in a mushroom salsa. The waiters will be able to explain exactly what goes into these dishes. The mouthwatering translations serve to give customers much more of an interest in the food they are about to eat.

Couscous aux Crevettes

A sauté of fresh shrimp tails and mussels tossed with tomato spiced with harissa and rolled durum wheat, served with a pickled ginger and tomato sauce.

Reverie du Sud

A thin omelette with artichoke bottoms cooked in olive oil and balsamic vinegar, sun-dried tomatoes and marinated shitaki mushrooms.

Filets Mignon à la Fleur de Thym et aux Champignons

Two thyme-marinated fillet steaks grilled and served on Pommes Anna with a mushroom salsa.

Glossary of Cooking terms

Some of the terms used on menus might seem intimidating if you have no idea what they mean. Ask your waiter to explain; it's vital for your health to know what goes into your food.

Americaine: Good Mediterranean style of cooking seafood, usually lobster or monkfish in olive oil, herbs, white wine, fish stock, brandy and tarragon.

Baste: Watch out for meat which has been basted in its own fats or butter. It is often used to moisten meat before and during roasting, grilling or barbecueing.

Blanch: Putting food into cold water to remove salt, starch or other flavours which need to be toned down. Some vegetables may be blanched in boiling water before further cooking, or to heighten their colour before serving almost raw. Good and healthy, unless your chef covers the vegetables in butter to add shine before serving. Most chefs won't use oil for serving because it doesn't emulsify with the water the vegetables have just been cooked in. Encourage your chef to serve them without butter or oil.

Bonne Femme: Good rustic style of serving traditional French food such as chicken with bacon, potatoes and baby onions. Literally means 'housewife'.

Bordelaise: Dishes made with Bordeaux wine and shallots.

Bourguignonne: Dishes cooked in Burgundy wine with onions, mushrooms and ham.

Braise: Slow cooking in a large pot usually with stock or wine. The meat might well be browned in fat first, and the dish benefits from cooking in its own fats and juices. Not a great Mediterranean Health Diet method of cooking.

Cacciatora: Literally means 'hunter-style', and refers to Italian dishes of game and poultry which are cooked in wine, mushrooms and tomatoes. The meat will probably be quite lean. In French, the dish is called 'chasseur'.

Carpaccio: Thinly sliced raw fillet of beef, either served with cream, as was the original, made famous in Harry's Bar in Venice in the early sixties or, preferably, marinated in olive oil and lemon juice.

Confit: Means 'preserve'. Meat such as duck or goose will be cooked very slowly in its own fat until tender, and covered so that it is not in contact with air.

Coulis: A thin purée of vegetables or fruit – pure and simple and looks great on the plate.

Emulsion: A mixture of two liquids which do not mix – e.g. oil and water. Some chefs are worried about using oils because they are visible on the surface if water has been used in the cooking. Once we learn that olive oil is extremely tasty as well as being very good for us, we won't mind about seeing it in soups. Needless to say, the Mediterraneans don't worry about visible oils.

Florentine: A dish made or garnished with spinach.

Fricassée: A dish in which meat such as poultry might be bound with a white or velouté sauce. Generally read as 'creamy'.

Genovese: An Italian style of cooking with olive oil, herbs and garlic.

Gratin: Cooked in the oven or under the grill developing a crust. It may refer to a cheese and breadcrumb topping which forms the crust.

Jardinière: Garnished with vegetables from the garden – often turnips, carrots and other root vegetables.

Lyonnaise: A dish garnished with onions. Lyon is one of the gastronomic capitals of the world and is synonymous with cream sauces. Check with your waiter.

Marengo: Veal or chicken cooked in olive oil, tomatoes and garlic and often garnished with deep-fried eggs, crayfish and croûtons.

Marinara: Literally means 'sailor style' and can refer to any combination of ingredients. Usually seafood-based with white wine, shallots and herbs.

Milanese: Like Marinara, it doesn't refer to a specific set of ingredients. The French use the term to mean a pasta dish with cheese, tomatoes and mushrooms.

Niçoise: A Mediterranean dish of tuna, tomatoes, garlic and black olives with anchovies and green beans.

Normande: Fish or seafood with a white wine cream sauce, Calvados and apple. Try it without the cream.

Papillotte: Cooking in oiled or greaseproof paper. For possibly the easiest fish dish, see Andy Magson's Truite en Papillotte Citronée on page 220.

Paprika: Hungarian goulash with a thick pink sauce of paprika and soured cream.

Parmigiana: A Mediterranean dish containing Parmesan cheese and, frequently, Prosciutto ham.

Pot roast: See 'braise' – again watch out for the fat content.

Provençale: Good Mediterranean area of France where the cooking relies on olives and their oil for a strongly flavoured variety of dishes. Lots of herbs and tomatoes.

Ragoût: Posh word for stew.

Roulade: A piece of meat, fish or pastry, rolled with a sweet or savoury filling. If savoury, it may be braised or poached. Check out the fillings and the amount of fat with your waiter.

Salsa: Sauce from Italy or Mexico. The juice is gathered from the principal ingredient such as the meat and used as a sauce. In South America it often refers to a spicy accompaniment to corn chips.

Sauté: Cooking small pieces of food quickly in very hot oil or butter. Very small pieces of vegetables might absorb a lot of fat. Also refers to dishes started over high heat, and finished in the same pan with added white wine and herbs, stock and other liquids to steam.

Savoury: Highly seasoned final course in traditional English dinner. Scotch Woodcock is the most Mediterranean, meaning scrambled eggs with anchovy.

Sear: Cooking meat or vegetables over high heat to seal in the juices.

Souse: **Covering food such as fish with wine vinegar.**
Stir fry: **The healthier version of sautéing, using less fat and tossing the food before it absorbs the fat.**
Tempura: **Japanese word for deep frying.**

Stephen Terry recently opened The Canteen, Marco Pierre White as a brasserie version of the award-winning Harvey's. While Marco bellowed about the limitations nutritional guidelines place on chefs – yet claims as his signature dish the more than acceptable Tagliatelle with Oysters and Caviar – Stephen Terry agreed that chefs have changed their attitude to food. 'People tend to think of haute cuisine as heavy,' he says. 'They associate it with *foie gras* and cream sauces. But what more and more chefs are doing is moving towards olive oils and away from animal fats. We're encouraging people to learn about the different flavours olive oils offer by putting a dish of it on the table for people to dip their bread into before they start their meal. People tend to think more about what they're putting into their bodies these days and look to chefs like us to show them really interesting ways to prepare healthy food.' A selection of Stephen Terry's recipes is on pages 251-63.

This may be true of a growing band of more health-conscious restaurant goers, but Eugene McCoy of McCoy's Tontine in Staddlebridge in Yorkshire believes that it is going to take a while before the health message hits home to many chefs. 'It's a question of commercial pressures,' he told us from the Bohemian sitting-room in the Tontine restaurant which has been described as Yorkshire's answer to Langan's. 'My brother Tom can cook what he likes in the restaurant, and get away with it, but what I cook for the bistro customer downstairs is down to what sells. This area is very tough, and the people are very stubborn in their ways, so we have to rely on cooking simple dishes with the best possible ingredients and stick on a couple of frilly corners. Take the Mediterranean prawns which we marinate with garlic, capsicum and capers – we'll sell two tonight, and the rest of our customers will go for the steak au poivre. People like creamy sauces around here – they go for what they wouldn't necessarily cook at home.'

When pressed, Eugene admitted to using a selection of fine olive oils, and claimed to be one of the first in the area to use oils with fish. 'All these trendy dishes of red mullet, or sea bass with black and green olives, might have started cropping up on the menus of London restaurants, but you saw them first here at the Tontine two years ago,' he insisted. 'And we haven't had chips on the menu once in seventeen years.'

In fact, looking through that night's menu showed more than a passing flirtation with the Mediterranean Health Diet: halibut with wild mushroom sauce; fresh lemon and Dover sole; aubergine, baked with cheese and tomato sauce; a savoury tomato and red pepper tart with anchovies and cheese; and a salad of haricots vert, tuna and garlic sausage. And when pressed to name his fantasy foods, Eugene tended towards the fish dishes without sauces. 'You get a bit sick of rich food after a while. I love to marry good wine with good food. If I'd made a fish dish with coriander, veal stock and chicken stock with red and green chillis, green capsicum, garlic and bean sprouts. I'd serve it with something like an Alsace Sylvaner.' He disappeared into the kitchen and emerged with a bottle of Mâcon-Lie and a selection of *crostini* with green, red and yellow peppers with olive oil, followed by pan-fried salmon with basil and chilli for us to tuck into. 'I might have to serve that with a cream sauce if I were to put it on the menu here,' he admitted. 'But this is something I do at home for the family – the kids love the bite of the chilli.'

The McCoy brothers are typical of the breed of chefs who were inspired by their mothers' or grandmothers' cooking, and who were encouraged to be creative with the cheapest foods out of necessity. 'We were vegetarians when we were lads,' said Eugene 'because meat was so expensive. If we weren't imaginative with a salad, we'd have been eating beans on toast all the time. When we first started off here, Tom used to make us fantastic omelettes with Parmesan which we'd nick from the restaurant.' A selection of McCoy's Tontine recipes is on pages 283-5.

Just down the road in Harrogate, Simon Gueller bases his menu on the food of the South of France. He prefers to use oils to animal fats. 'If people knew how bad those fats are for them, they wouldn't want them,' he told us. 'I try to go out of my way to create dishes in which I use completely different ingredients. I might be cutting my repertoire in half by not filling the menu with cream-based dishes, and a wide repertoire is supposed to be the making of a good chef, but I don't want to have to cook for the sake of it.' Simon is a rare chef – someone who at twenty-seven has earned a reputation for being a great cook, yet who will not be swayed by public demand in what Eugene McCoy insists is a tough area. 'I have to admit that most of my customers have 081 or 071 numbers,' he said. 'The locals just don't like my food.' A matter of getting used to different styles of cooking perhaps? 'Well, take my potato purée,' (we did) 'Most people would call it mashed potato, and whisk it with butter. I choose the type of potato carefully, add olive oil and put it in a blender. The potato has to be the right one for the gluten to come out. You can loosen it with a little low-fat milk, but as it's for the consistency rather than the flavour, you can just as well use water or stock, depending on how you want it to taste. Serve it with wild mushrooms or a salmon roasted with basil and sun-dried tomatoes, and you've got a wonderfully tasty dish that's really good for you.' A selection of Simon Gueller's recipes is on pages 276-82.

Testimony of a Business Luncher

Laurence Isaacson is a businessman whose working day often includes two meals out. He became very overweight by the age of 48 weighing 99kg – that's 15½ stone. With the help of Dr Ralph Abrahams at the London Diet and Lipid Centre who found that his cholesterol was dangerously high at 9 mmol/L, the doctor put him on a Mediterranean-style diet, substituting olive oil for butter and fish and poultry for steak and chips. Isaacson was thrilled to find that he could eat pasta and an endless variety of sauces and fresh foods, and still lose 1 stone 5 lb (9kg) over four months. Abrahams insisted that he eat a proper breakfast, and encouraged him to have his main meal at lunchtime so that he would work it off during the day. Four months later, without a single drug, his cholesterol had dropped to 5.5 mmol/L and he had cleared the danger zone. Restaurants owned by Isaacson include Soho Soho which boasts the first Mediterranean Diet menu in town.

While the latest offerings of *haute cuisine* may make you feel great, they might not, however, do much for your bank balance. Chefs such as Simon Gueller use top-quality ingredients which cost a fortune, and apply the sort of imagination not generally found in more affordable restaurants. But it is perfectly possible to get fresh food and a great meal in plenty of restaurants for a good price.

Lebanese, North African and Greek food are all part of the Mediterranean Diet, and many dishes are vegetarian. 'Meat is often too expensive for people to buy regularly,' explained Freddie Kojuman, the Iraqi-born restaurateur at The Olive Tree just off London's Leicester Square (see recipes on pages 322-9). The menu here is broadly Israeli, although many of the dishes can be found in Lebanese,

Turkish and Greek restaurants. 'We all tend to use a lot of chick-peas, lentils and rice,' said Freddie, 'but each country adapts the flavour just a little bit according to different traditions. In Israel, we don't eat milk with meat, so our Kushary is a bed of rice with vegetables and yoghurt while Lebanese restaurants might serve it with meat.'

Anna Lymbouri and her husband Panikos run Daphne's restaurant in Camden Town, North London. Greek food is often discredited as being nothing more inventive than moussaka and stuffed vine leaves swimming in oil, but Anna gave us a selection of vegetarian dishes which would make the heartiest meat eaters salivate. 'A lot of Greek restaurants in Britain are run by Greek-Cypriots who have a mixed culture as far as food is concerned,' explained Anna. Again, expense is a problem for many families living in the poorer areas, and lentils and pulses are often the staple diet. 'My family has been cooking these dishes for generations,' Anna told us. 'But I also use cookbooks like Rena Salaman's. It's easy enough to think about stuffed tomatoes and feta with aubergines, but we all need ideas, and luckily there are plenty around in the books nowadays.' A selection of recipes from Daphne's is on pages 330-2.

Using your Waiters

For many restaurateurs, cooking is their life. For some it is an art, while for others, food has been at the heart of their family and culture for generations. All of them will appreciate your interest in their food, and may show you more hospitality than they might choose to lavish on their less committed customers.

– Ask your waiter about the oils used in food, and whether fried means deep fried. The fat is more likely to be absorbed into your food if it's deep fried, while pan frying is often so quick that the fat barely touches the sides.

– If you are ordering something which is going to be fried in oil, ask the chef to use olive oil. It will be a rare kitchen which doesn't have at least one bottle in its cupboards.

– Don't be intimidated by your waiters; their job is to look after you and your needs. If you don't want butter on your vegetables, tell them.

___

If you're eating out, you are hardly going to turn down one of the delicious desserts wheeled in front of you by your now terribly friendly waiter. And why should you? Maddalena Bonino, the chef at Bertorelli's in London's Covent Garden, explained to us the Italian approach to puddings. 'Normally we don't eat them. After a meal, we drink coffee, and maybe eat some fruit, and on special occasions we eat the most wonderful cakes. We see it as pure indulgence, and appreciate it so much more if we keep it to special days such as Sundays or birthdays. So there's no such thing as a healthy pudding – they *must* be full of cream – what's the point otherwise?'

Luckily, while most of us would agree, Roger Pisey at Harvey's is busy making a raspberry terrine in champagne, Tony Howarth is putting the final touch to his Assiette des Fruits Exotiques and Simon Gueller is grilling his Gratin of Oranges. So, will the nutritionists let us eat cake or is it fruit all the way to a healthy heart? Nutritionist Valerie Clegg thinks that while puddings are a difficult area, there are plenty of delicious options. 'The alternatives to cream, like *fromage frais* and yoghurts, are really low in fat and, served with fruits, are wonderful. OK, so it is hard to steer away from fruits, but why would you want to? Try a summer pudding or filo pastry brushed with a tiny bit of olive oil and filled with fruit and *fromage frais*. The pastry itself doesn't have any fat in it at all. Fools and meringues which use egg whites and no hint of fat are very good too.'

Fat Guide to Cream and its Substitutes
Fromage Frais

Plain: 7 per cent
Fruit: 5.8 per cent
Very low: 0.2 per cent. Roughly half the fat is saturated

Yoghurt with its live bacteria has been known to be an important aid to digestion since Biblical times. Legend has it that the recipe was first disclosed to Abraham by an angel. Non-quiche eating men who think yoghurt is a bit girly might prefer the story that it was discovered by a courier of Genghis Khan's. Unfriendly villagers filled his water gourd with milk, hoping that it would go bad in the desert leaving him to die of thirst. Instead, the milk turned into a white substance which the courier found gave him renewed energy to reach Khan and his Mongolian forces, and yoghurt was born.

Yoghurt

Greek: 7.5 per cent
Plain: 1.5 per cent
Low fat: 0.8 per cent

Bio yoghurt is one of the latest ideas to arrive on the back of the healthier dairy products initiative. The *Biffidus* bacteria is an active ingredient which aids digestion and is said to be a major contribution to the prevention of stomach cancer.

Bio Yoghurt (we used Danone as an example)
Natural low fat: 1.5g per 100g of which 60 per cent saturated and 40 per cent polyunsaturated
Fruit full fat: 3.6g per 100g of which 60 per cent saturated and 40 per cent polyunsaturated

Cream

Single: 19.1 per cent
Whipping: 40 per cent
Double: 48 per cent

Crème Fraîche

Imported from France, this is a cream product and has roughly the same fat content as double and whipping cream.

OUT TO LUNCH

Eating out also covers the daily sandwiches, burgers, crisps and chips we call lunch. By the time you reach this chapter, there's no excuse whatsoever for watching your local sandwich maker loading the butter on to white bread. You can ask specifically for a selection of ingredients which will make a tasty, filling and healthy meal.

School children and hospital patients are not quite so lucky. Their caterers receive subsidies of up to eighty per cent for saturated fat products such as full-fat cheese, butter and milk, and with finances on the critical list, they claim to have both arms tied. Senior catering officer at what was ILEA, Robin Jenkins, told us about the lack of political commitment to healthy eating. 'The local authorities want to keep the school catering services in house, and healthy eating is low on the list of priorities while they're struggling against cuts and closures. Add to that the innate hostility between caterers and nutritionists, and there's not much chance of a change in direction. Staff are employed according to the demands in the kitchen and dining-room, and if children are refusing to eat school meals because chips are off the menu, the staff are going to be laid off too. The irony is that the only answer is to give your child a packed lunch, and that doesn't require the catering services at all.'

Last year Tim Laing from Parents for Safe Food launched a campaign backed by the British Medical Association and the Women's Institute to persuade the Government, parents and schools to apply healthy eating standards to school meals. 'The good news is that the Government is beginning to recognize its responsibilities to ensure that caterers play their part in achieving national health guidelines,' he told us. 'Schools have a huge responsibility to promote public health. The big question is whether these fine intentions will be put into practice at a local level and whether the Government will back its promises nationally. We have to give a priority to giving children good food in school so that they eat well throughout their lives. It's too easy for Government to say that it's the individual responsibility of parents to make sure their children eat properly.'

While any parent who cares at all about the health of their child must apply pressure to raise the standard of school meals, a packed lunch is an interim answer. A midday meal is the most important, especially for children who will expend more energy during the rest of the day. Sandwiches are a good all-round meal with enough carbohydrates to fuel a child's energy, and can be made with a low-fat polyunsaturated margarine instead of butter. Fruit, salads, pasta, or leftovers from last night's vegetable bake, will all taste so much better and do so much more good than a packet of crisps. 'Children's eating standards in school are back to the way they were in the thirties,' Robin Jenkins told us. 'It's an absolute scandal that they're not getting enough energy or calcium in their food.' While the local authorities wage war with the private sector, which has yet to prove a real commitment to health, the onus weighs on us, the parents, to give our children a decent midday meal.

CHAPTER 7

Kicking the Habit

PL

This final chapter before the mouth-watering recipe section is for those of us who have a problem. If you are used to eating badly, if you are overweight through eating the wrong foods or you simply eat too much, then this chapter is for you. If, however, you are one of the few people who can eat as much as you like, are naturally attuned to your body's nutritional needs and have never eaten a whole bar of chocolate after being blown out on a date, then skip to the next section – we don't know people like you . . .

If you're like most people, there's going to be one thing that's nagging away, urging you on to do something about your bad habits at one point and then casting a cloud of despair over you at the next. It is a very simple fly in the ointment, and one which salesmen, psychologists and parents know all too well – fear of change.

Most people hate change; at worst they're terrified, at best they find it a chore. The Mediterranean Health Diet encourages you to change your eating habits completely for the rest of your life. You're going to stop thinking about meat as the principal ingredient on your plate with a couple of frozen peas and some chips around the side for a bit of colour and stodge. You're going to think twice before sticking your head in the freezer and coming out with a selection of beefburgers and pies for the family. You're going to cook again after *how* many years of microwaving ready-meals and baking oven chips?

If you're a foodie, you're half-way there. You are not the victim of advertising campaigns which drum home the idea that food is the enemy of the perfect figure. You may well be one of the post-war generation who learned to eat everything on your plate because, after years of rationing and austerity Scarlett O' Hara style, you were never going to be hungry again.

Ask yourself how many objections your family and friends have put up when you've told them they should think about changing to the Mediterranean Health Diet. They may have said that they can't stick to any diet other than their own, or that their fry-ups are the one luxury they have in their life. They may have said that they don't like olive oil or vegetables, but eventually confess that they've never really tried the type of dishes featured in the second part of this book. They may have said that it would be too expensive but have no idea how much it would really cost.

Worst of all is the overweight, red-faced food addict who says that he or she would prefer to die from a heart attack rather than change to the Mediterranean Health Diet. It might sound like a quick end to a life of over-indulgence, but the reality of a heart attack is very different. If you've just had a heart attack, you're likely to be a man of about forty-five with two or three children and a wife. They'll all be watching your every movement after you come out of intensive care, terrified that you're going to peg out on them. Your wife will probably take it upon herself to feed you properly, and will feel personally responsible if you don't make it. So forget this idea that one day you're just going to keel over and slip off into the next life accompanied by a concerto of celestial violins.

This chapter will tell you what to expect from someone who is determined to scupper your chances of success, especially if that person is you. It will explain why you have always failed on those crash diets and how much your body will respond if you exercise it. It accepts the brain as a complex organ which fires messages at us which we *know* are bad for us, and also looks at the rather more complicated issues surrounding food and addiction. Most importantly, it will show you that you're not on your own in being frightened of change, and that you're among a rising number of people who are ready to do something about it.

THE DEMONS WITHIN

Despite the common sense principles of the Mediterranean Health Diet – enjoying food and a more relaxed attitude to life – we all know that following common sense is not always the easiest thing to do. Most of us have demons screaming for chocolate when we least need it, and our minds are far too devious to listen to the sensible warnings our bodies give when we're set on a path of self-abuse. Eating is about so much more than simple nutritional needs; cravings for comfort foods often disguise serious psychological problems, while new healthy regimes are often just too tempting for our mental devils to leave alone.

We're clever enough to think of any number of excuses for our bad habits. The chocolate industry has boasted huge increases in sales during the recession with thirty more tonnes disappearing into our downturned mouths than five years ago. United Biscuits' profits rose eight per cent in the penny-pinching months of 1991. A spokesman from Terry's chocolates was even looking forward to a nineteen per cent increase in sales in the next four years. Maybe he knows something the Chancellor doesn't. And while we're saving on the restaurant bills, supermarkets have noticed that our little demons are enticing us with 'comfort food' in the form of ready meals – particularly those nice rich Indian microwave dishes in which butter, cream and sugars revel in their 'luxury food' status.

Even though our need for calories is less now than ever before with technology taking care of most of our physical duties, we continue to cram in the cakes, believing that our bodies are shouting for them. When we were growing up, we needed far more calories than we do now. The success of the Mediterranean Health Diet is in the eating rather than the calorie counting. It may help at first to make sure that you correct your intake level to a healthy one, but remember – obsession makes you fat.

When you change your whole family's eating habits with the Mediterranean Diet, you may find that you're in competition with at least one member of the family to lose weight. Despite women being generally more aware of health issues, men are the ones who tend to lose weight and stick to a changed regime. They tend to take more exercise too, although with less information about nutrition than their female friends. They often cut out on the bread and potatoes that are essential as carbohydrates for providing the fuel to burn their fat. Women often have a lower self-esteem than men and take to snacking despite knowing the pitfalls. Women tend to drink and smoke more too, which can make their men seem irritatingly self-righteous if they are succeeding in changing their old habits on the Mediterranean Diet.

Dave Mela from the Institute of Food Research in Reading is conducting a study which looks at why we seem to be so resistant to nutritional advice. 'We've all taken on board the messages about milk, and sales of semi-skimmed milk have soared over the past ten years. And we're really proud of ourselves; every time we have a cup of tea, we remind ourselves of just how good we're being. Unfortunately we're so pleased with ourselves that we go and buy a chocolate bar. It's madness, but we all do it. How many times have you bought a Diet Coke and a Snickers?'

Mela and his researchers have found that people are still very confused about fat intake. When asked how much fat they thought was in a pint of beer, his survey sample answered between fifteen and seventy-five per cent. The answer is nil, but the range of answers shows how little information is getting through despite the urgent tabloid headlines and endless Government leaflets. And there we have the reason for the nation's health problem; if it's too hard to understand, we can't be bothered.

The Mediterranean Health Diet with its simple policy of eating more fresh fruits, vegetables and starchy food like pasta, cutting out butter, cream and full-fat milk, answers the nutritional advice on cutting down on fat intake while distracting us from the idea of it being a diet at all. Have a quick look at all the delicious recipes in the second half of the book to remind yourself of just how punishing this change is going to be . . . Losing weight on the Mediterranean Health Diet is simply about reducing the intake of the sort of nutrients which provide the most calories. If you remember that they are carbohydrates, fat and alcohol, you won't even think about counting calories.

How to Reduce Fats in Your Diet

Try not to eat too much saturated (animal) fat
  – **Chicken skin**
  – **Butter, cream, full-fat milk**
  – **Fatty meat**

Buy lean meats, particularly poultry, and remove the skin, add herbs, or casserole with lots of flavour, and you'll find you don't miss the fat at all.

Eat more fish. White fish is low in fat and oily fish is rich in unsaturated fat which is good for the heart.

Choose soft cheeses rather than hard cheese like ched-

dar. Camembert, Brie and cottage cheese are much lower in fat.

Learn to use low-fat yoghurt instead of double cream in recipes or as toppings

If you need milk, use the low-fat varieties.

Use olive oil rather than butter. You won't use as much and it's much better for your heart. Remember that olive oil is still fattening if you use too much.

More than eighty per cent of the calories we consume come from these three, so keep them in check and the calories will look after themselves. And by introducing olive oil into your diet and doing without a lot of those old dairy products, you're going to be doing your heart a lot of good before you even eat your first roasted pepper.

How to Reduce Sugars

Eat fruit rather than sweets.

Use ginger, lemon or cinnamon to sweeten food in cooking.

Dried fruits are also good sweeteners and provide other essential nutrients.

Look out for hidden sugars in foods you haven't prepared yourself: biscuits, sweetened breakfast cereals and canned drinks will often have a high sugar content – look out for high calorie count in the nutritional information, or buy from the Co-op where they use different labelling which is much clearer, marking 'high sugar' and 'low sugar'.

Look for diet versions of canned drinks.

After only a few days your palate will start to adapt to a lack of sugar in your diet, so don't believe the demons within who convince you that you've got a sweet tooth – there's no such thing.

WHY HAVE I ALWAYS FAILED ON CRASH DIETS?

Crash dieters expect much and usually get nothing other than a severe case of the doldrums. Most people who follow these diets are overweight and well used to self-abuse; the fit of depression and lack of self-worth following another slimming failure are almost a foregone conclusion. Your body rebels against the sudden strict regime, while your brain is reminding you of messages from your childhood, like the existence of sweets you can eat between meals without ruining your appetite. If your mind and body are both screaming resistance, who is it that wants to be on this crash diet?

In the first stages of a slimming diet, people often lose a great deal of weight which levels off after the first few weeks. It is after this point that it becomes difficult to shift the pounds, you give up and depression sets in. What has happened in those first few weeks is that the body has shed water, glycogen and protein rather than excess fat. Once back to your old eating habits, the body fluids are replaced and you put the weight back on. Sounds familiar? Worse is to come. Each time you put your body through this ordeal, your metabolic rate will fall, along with your calorie requirement and your body gives up the ghost, becoming flabbier, loading on the fat more quickly and refusing steadfastly to lose weight again.

FLAB FACTS

When you start cutting down on your intake, the body, ever on its guard to defend against what it sees as danger, immediately responds by shutting off access to the fat stores to save calories. The muscles are weakened, and valuable muscle tissue is lost. In other words, you'll become flabby. Not exactly what you had in mind, but if you combine this reduction of calories with the Mediterranean Health Diet and exercise, you can't help but lose weight. By burning more calories and using up more of the body's store of fat, you're doing exactly the opposite of what you were doing on your crash diet. With extra muscle using more energy than fat, you're also much more likely to stay slim. One thing to point out though is that muscle weighs more than tissue, so for the first week or so of jogging, swimming or any other muscle-building exercise, don't be surprised if you put on a couple of pounds. This will right itself as you continue to burn up the fat.

EXERCISE AND THE HAPPY-DRUG

Probably the best news this book can give you is that there is an alternative to chocolate which will give you the same high – if not better – as well as steering you towards optimum health. When you exercise, the brain releases natural hormones which are called endorphins and mimic the action of morphine. Needless to say, these 'happy-drugs' induce a feeling of well-being while also acting as a mild pain suppressant. They also help you sleep better, and encourage a more enjoyable sex life.

Jamie Addicoat, the Australian Fatbuster who has terrorized many a slothful Brit into changing their body-shape once and for all, explained how exercise can help an active sex life. 'Well, think about it, you're going to be more confident because you're not wobbling all over the place for a start. Women are automatically going to tighten up all those important bits – inside and out. And men will increase their stamina – they may need it if they want to handle the increased sexual appetite their women are going to have.'

Exercise curbs the appetite too by preventing a drop in the blood sugar levels caused by hunger. It increases your metabolic rate, meaning that your food is digested more quickly and calories burn up more efficiently. It builds firmer muscle tissue while burning the fat, meaning that you are more likely to look slimmer permanently. With the Mediterranean Health Diet, you'll find that you will lose weight quickly at first, especially if you are replacing a regular fried feast. Your body will find its own natural weight, and probably stick to it.

We do not recommend a calorie-controlled diet because we believe that it takes all the enjoyment out of eating, and can make you obsessive. But, some doctors suggest that it can be a good gauge to people who haven't a clue about how much to eat, or need the discipline to lose weight. If you do not want to count the calories on the Mediterranean Health Diet and combine it with a strict exercise routine so that you are burning more calories than you're taking in, remember that olive oil is fattening if taken in high quantities.

You can exercise at any age, but if you are overweight with high blood pressure and planning to end a lifetime of sloth with a couple of games of squash, think again; no amount of olive oil is going to prevent you from keeling over from a major heart attack. Start gradually with an exercise which you will want to continue. Endorphins may be released by jogging, but there are plenty of people who can't get beyond the first cramps, stitch and pure agony to enjoy the highs. Fast walking, swimming and cycling are all extremely good aerobic exercises for people of all ages. If you don't think you have time for exercise, or simply can't be bothered, think about what it does for your heart, and maybe you will be able to find the energy from somewhere.

SOUL FOOD

As we in the Western world gradually realize how out of touch we are with our bodies, increasing numbers of yoga teachers, homeopaths and healers are offering an alternative to the high impact, sweat-till-you-drop theory of fitness. Joy Anderson is an ex-aerobics teacher who has found a gentler form of exercise in yoga. One of the first aerobics teachers in Britain, Joy filled classes with over 150 people in South London fifteen years ago. As her pupils delighted in their rampant endorphins and new bodies, Joy's success was echoed in fitness centres throughout the country. But it all went horribly wrong five years ago when her body became so tight that she lost nearly all the mobility in her right side, forcing her to give up her teaching and to find a form of exercise that would correct her back before she became a cripple. 'It changed my whole way of thinking about exercise and what we do to our bodies to make them look good,' she said. 'If you're overweight, then aerobics classes where you're jumping about for an hour is the last thing you should do. Think about the strain you'd be putting on your joints. But it is vitally important to keep the heart healthy. Walking quickly is an excellent exercise and anyone can do it anywhere. Swimming is the best way to get fit if you're overweight because it is an aerobic exercise and so it gets the heart working harder and burns off the fat, but at least the water is supporting the body.'

Joy now holds yoga classes where people of all ages with mixed mobility learn to stretch, lengthening muscles, increasing flexibility and relieving most forms of joint problems from arthritis to curvature of the spine and bunions. Strangely enough, breathing seems to be the key to moving the bits you never thought you'd move again. 'Try it,' said Joy. 'Stand up as tall as you can and breath really deeply. When you breathe out, empty your abdomen and notice just how differently it feels to the way you normally breathe. We tend to breathe using the lung tissue in the front of our bodies whereas most of it is in our backs. You'll probably find that your back clicks and your lungs wheeze; if you're prepared to ignore that, then prepare yourself for becoming old before your time.' Anyone who is already feeling old before their time might want to read Vita Scaravelli's *Awakening the Spine* in which the eighty-three-year-old author demonstrates the sort of postures you probably weren't even doing at twenty-three.

As with most of the more alternative exercise teachers, Joy understands the real problems dictating her pupils' body shape. And it's not just the hopeless fatties who are so see-through. 'People tend to become obsessed by exercise,' she says. 'You'll often find die-hard joggers will get fidgety and uptight if they don't run every day; it tends to hide the real issues behind their obsession. Having said that, if the alternative is to stuff their faces with cream cakes, then obviously they're better off jogging, but they should make sure they see it as an obsession and therefore a problem.'

The compulsion to abuse ourselves through over-exercising, lack of exercise and bad eating habits is very probably a deep-rooted, psychological imbalance, and one which a growing number of people around the world are beginning to accept as such. Homeopath Jane Temple says that many of her patients who come to see her about insomnia, stress or obesity are very often suffering from eating disorders. 'Homeopathy deals with the person as a complex jigsaw, whose experiences from childhood into adulthood have influenced him or her on a far deeper level than we may realize. It then understands that the body is in most instances entirely capable of healing itself, as long as it is put back on the track any number of circumstances could have forced it from.' Following this principle, your flabby, unfit body which suffers from the ravaging effects of arthritis and insomnia, is perfectly able to heal itself. On condition that you feed and exercise it properly, and face some of the horrors that your uncon-scious mind may be hiding from you, it will find its own natural shape and weight.

Jane Temple gave us an example of some of the problems she comes across. 'Illnesses very obviously related to food, such as anorexia and bulimia, are often nothing to do with a love or hate of food itself. It's more about over-indulgence and denial of very deep-seated emotions, which might be triggered off by food. If you think about food as nourishment, people who were denied love as a child may overcompensate as adults. A strong craving for sweet things might be symbolic of a deep need for affection.' Jane says that people come to her for advice on diet, and often feel that changing their eating habits gives them back the control over their health which they felt they had lost. They see it as the first step on a path of greater self-awareness,' she told us.

If you think you have a food disorder, whether it's just a habit of eating every time you're frustrated, unhappy or angry, or a more serious compulsion like bingeing and vomiting or starving yourself, see a dietitian. Your GP will be able to recommend one, and they are absolutely free.

If you have simply been unaware of good food and the joys of eating well all this time, then celebrate *tonight* by cooking one of the delicious meals in the next section. Look through your larder *now* and throw out all the biscuits, sweets and chocolate. Get out a bowl and put some fruit on the table. You're more likely to be tempted to tuck into a peach if it's staring you in the face, and you won't allow it to lose its nutrient value if you notice how many days it's been sitting there. Get to know the markets nearby – *walk* there if you can. Make friends with your greengrocer, your butcher and your fishmonger, demand a little more of them, and let a little continental Europe into your world.

PART 2

Recipes

What has particularly delighted us in writing this book is the variety of restaurants, kitchens and family dining-rooms that we have found ourselves in. We witnessed three generations of cooks in Southern Italy arguing about the best way of making tomato sauce, olive sellers in the South of France passionately discussing tapenade, which contrasted with the simple genius of Britain's best chefs.

Home Cooking

ITALY

Our hosts in Acciaroli in Southern Italy were keen to teach us the recipes which had passed down to them over the years. The methods caused howls of disapproval and much arm waving from friends who insisted that their grandmothers made the quintessential Caponata/Ciambotta etc. Our pens poised, we listened closely to the 90 mph Italian, and came away with the following recipes.

Pesto Sauce

This is traditionally made with a pestle and mortar, but works well in a blender or food processor.

MAKES 15 FL OZ (450 ML)
1½ oz (40 g) basil leaves, washed and drained
6 garlic cloves, peeled
1½ oz (40 g) pine kernels
6 fl oz (175 ml) olive oil
salt to taste
4 oz (100 g) Parmesan cheese, finely grated

If using a blender or food processor, mix on a slow speed. Put the first five ingredients into the blender and mix well. Pour into a bowl and mix in the cheese by hand.

Wine: A red or white such as Montepulciano d'Abruzzo or Orvieto Secco.

Aubergine Moussaka

Moussaka is probably thought of as a Greek dish, but it is also one of the best-loved Italian meals.

SERVES 4–6

1 medium aubergine, about 1½ lb (700 g)
salt and pepper
1½ lb (700 g) potatoes, peeled
1–2 tbsp olive oil
1 lb (450 g) good tomatoes, sliced
2 garlic cloves, peeled and chopped finely
a handful of basil leaves, shredded
2 tsp fresh oregano leaves
about 2 oz (50 g) Cheddar-type cheese, grated (optional)

Slice the aubergine thinly, place in a sieve and sprinkle with salt. Leave for at least 30 minutes to allow the bitter juices to drain out. Meanwhile, slice the potatoes thinly.

Preheat the oven to 375°F (190°C) Gas 5.

Steam the rinsed and dried aubergine slices over boiling seasoned water until soft. Place the olive oil in a large baking dish. First, arrange a layer of aubergines, then layers of tomatoes, potatoes, garlic, herbs and seasoning. Finish with a layer of potatoes, and sprinkle with cheese, if liked. Bake in the oven for 1 hour or until hot and bubbling.

Wine: Either Barbera d'Alba or Barbera d'Asti – full reds with a slight 'bite'. Chianti Classico is another good quality red.

Minestrone di Verdure

SERVES 8

5 oz (150 g) dried haricot beans
4 tbsp olive oil
2 onions, peeled and diced
2 carrots, diced
4 celery sticks, sliced
1 garlic clove, peeled and crushed
2 leeks, sliced
5¼ pints (3 litres) chicken or vegetable stock
1 bay leaf
12 green beans
salt and pepper
1 small cauliflower, cut into small florets
3 oz (75 g) small macaroni
2 courgettes, chopped
3 tomatoes, skinned, seeded and chopped
2 tbsp chopped fresh basil or parsley
freshly grated Parmesan cheese, to taste

Soak the haricot beans for at least 6–8 hours, and then simmer in fresh water until tender, about 1–1½ hours. Take off the heat and leave to one side, still in the cooking liquid.

In a large pot, heat the oil and sauté the onions until soft. Add the carrot, celery, garlic and leek and sauté until browned. Add the stock, bay leaf and haricot beans with their liquid and bring to the boil. Add the green beans and seasoning. Cover and simmer for 5 minutes. Add the cauliflower and macaroni and continue until the pasta is *al dente*, about 10 minutes.

Add the courgettes and tomatoes, and simmer for about 5 minutes until tender. Remove the bay leaf, mix in the herbs, and serve with grated Parmesan cheese.

Wine: Either a Gewürztraminer from Alto Adige in North-Eastern Italy or a buttery creamy Chardonnay from the same region.

Sunday lunch in Acciaroli

The basis of this dish is the fruity tomato sauce on page 176. This can be simply used as a sauce for pasta, to be served with salad, or meat and other vegetables can be added to make a main meal as they do in Acciaroli. This takes the full four hours to cook. The Italians take the meat out and eat the sauce with pasta to start, followed by the meat.

SERVES 4
Fruity Tomato Sauce (see page 176)
2 tbsp extra virgin olive oil
1 large onion, peeled and sliced thinly
salt and pepper

Beef rolls

2 lb (900 g) silverside or rump of beef, cut into 8 thin slices
about 4 oz (100 g) firm goat's cheese, diced finely
1 small onion, peeled and diced finely
1 small carrot, peeled and diced finely
4 sage leaves, shredded

Make the tomato sauce first.

Heat the olive oil in a large lidded casserole and sauté the onion slowly.

Meanwhile, spread out the beef slices on a work surface. Mix the remaining beef roll ingredients together, season, and divide between the slices. Roll up and tie the rolls with string.

Remove the onion from the casserole, using a slotted spoon, and keep to one side. Fry the rolls in the oil in the pan until browned on all sides. Return the onion to the casserole and add the tomato sauce. Bring to a simmer, then cover and cook for up to 4 hours (at least 1½) on a very low heat.

Wine: A light easy drinking Galestro is good if meat is not
        included or, with meat, a serious wine such as
        Santa Cristina from Marchesi Antinori in Tuscany.

Caponata
Sicilian Ratatouille

A favourite of Professor Ancel and Margaret Keys, the couple who were responsible for recognizing the protective qualities of the Mediterranean Diet (see pp. 38-40). They eat this dish regularly at their home in the Cilento coast village of Pioppi.

SERVES 6–8

2 medium aubergines
salt and pepper
2 large onions, peeled and sliced
2 fl oz (50 ml) olive oil
1 lb (450 g) tomatoes, chopped
8 oz (225 g) celery, trimmed and sliced
2 fl oz (50 ml) white wine vinegar
2 tbsp drained capers
2 tbsp sugar
2 oz (50 g) olives, pitted and quartered
1 oz (25 g) blanched almonds, chopped, or pine kernels
2 tbsp chopped parsley

Cut the aubergines into small cubes, sprinkle with salt, and leave to drain of their bitter juices (at least 30 minutes).

Sauté the onion in the oil until soft, then add the tomatoes and celery and simmer for 20 minutes. Add the vinegar, capers, sugar, olives, almonds and seasoning. Rinse and dry the aubergine, and add to the mixture. Cover and simmer for 10 minutes. Stir in the parsley and serve cold.

Wine: A light Frascati is pleasant such as a Superiore or a dry red such as a Valpolicella from the hills above Verona.

Carciofi e Potati
Artichokes and Potatoes

One of Acciaroli's favourite contorni, or side dishes.
Serve cold.

SERVES 4–6

3–4 small artichokes
juice of ½ lemon
12 oz (350 g) potatoes, peeled
1 onion, peeled and chopped coarsely
1 garlic clove, peeled and crushed
2 tbsp olive oil
salt and pepper

Bend back and snap off the outer green part of the leaves
of the artichokes, until a central dome of leaves is formed.
Cut this off level with the topmost snapped leaves. Cut the
artichokes into half from top to bottom, and then into
quarters. Remove the bristly choke from each wedge, and
brush all cut surfaces with lemon juice to prevent discolor-
ation.

Cut the potatoes into large pieces. In a suitably sized
casserole, fry the potato pieces, onion and garlic in the oil.
When the potatoes are half cooked, add the artichoke
wedges, with a little water and some seasoning. Cover and
simmer until tender, turning occasionally, about 30–40
minutes.

Acciaroli Melanzane
Aubergines with Cheese

SERVES 4

2 medium aubergines
salt and pepper
about 2 tbsp extra virgin olive oil
1 lb (450 g) home-made Tomato Sauce (see page 176)
2 garlic cloves, peeled and crushed
1 Italian Mozzarella cheese, drained and grated coarsely
2 tbsp grated Parmesan cheese
2 tsp chopped basil leaves

Cut the aubergines into long thin slices, sprinkle with salt and drain for at least 30 minutes. Rinse, dry well, and brush a little olive oil on each side. Grill until golden.

Meanwhile, pre-heat the oven to 400°F (200°C) Gas 6.

Line the bottom of a suitably sized greased dish with a single layer of aubergine slices. Top with some of the tomato sauce, garlic, grated Mozzarella, Parmesan, herb and seasoning. Continue layering until all the ingredients are used up, finishing with aubergines and Parmesan. Drizzle with some more oil and bake in the oven for 20–30 minutes.

Wine: A Cabernet Sauvignon, a heavyweight rich red, would complement the richness of this recipe; or a soft and plummy Merlot.

Celso Vegetable Soup

This is also used as a stock or sauce for pasta. It makes use
of old beans and dry bread. Chick-peas can be used
instead of the dried beans.

SERVES 4

8 oz (225 g) dried beans or chick-peas
4 oz (100 g) brown or green lentils
2 onions, peeled and chopped finely
4 tbsp olive oil
2–3 tbsp home-made Tomato Sauce (see page 176)
2 tbsp chopped parsley
2 oz (50 g) goat's cheese, crumbled or diced
1 pint (600 ml) water or stock

Soak the beans or chick-peas and the lentils, separately, in
cold water overnight. The next day, rinse well, cover with
fresh water, and bring – again separately – to the boil.
Simmer the beans or chick-peas for about 1–1½ hours, the
lentils for 20 minutes, then drain.

Fry the onion in the oil in a large pan for a few minutes
to soften. Add the tomato sauce, the beans or chick-peas
and lentils, parsley, cheese and water. Simmer for 20
minutes.

Pour the soup over dry crusty bread or cooked pasta, or
use as a cooking medium for a meat casserole.

Wine: A light fresh red such as Bardolino from the
eastern edge of Lake Garda or a white from Siena
– Vernaccia di San Gimignano.

Ciambotta

SERVES 4–6

4 large new potatoes, scrubbed
2 small aubergines, cut into small chunks
4 medium tomatoes, quartered
2 medium courgettes, sliced thickly
2 medium onions, peeled and sliced thickly
about 6 tbsp olive oil
2 red peppers, roasted and skinned (see page 178)
salt and pepper
2 oz (50 g) basil leaves, shredded

Fry the first five ingredients separately in olive oil until nearly tender. Drain well and place in a dish. Add the roasted peppers, in chunks or strips, and mix. Season to taste, top with the basil and allow to cool.

Wine: A soft and fragrant red such as a Merlot perhaps from Veneto or a more robust red from Sicily – Corvo, Duca di Salaparuta.

Anna's Snack

Professor Anna Ferro-Luzzi, responsible for the study of the Mediterranean Diet in Celso (see pp. 39-40), suggests a wonderfully nutritious sandwich for any time of the day.

'I make myself a sandwich like this at least a couple of times a week. It's absolutely delicious, cheap, very filling and gives me the mono-unsaturated fat, the Vitamin C and beta carotene I need. Try to buy the tomatoes with the very strong smell. The watery bigger ones just don't have the flavour.'

PER PERSON

1 slice brown bread
½–1 garlic clove, crushed, to taste
about 1 tbsp extra virgin olive oil
about 4 cherry tomatoes
2 tsp chopped fresh oregano
salt and pepper

Toast the bread lightly on one side, then spread the untoasted side with the crushed garlic and drizzle with the olive oil. Slice the tomatoes on top and sprinkle with oregano and seasoning to taste. Eat with a knife and fork.

Wine: A beefy red such as Cirò Rosso from Calabria or a Chardonnay.

FRANCE

Our research also took us to the borders of Provence and the Domaine Gournier vineyard, where owner Maurice Barnouin showed us how the locals eat. Olive oil is everywhere, with many people making their own, using the local cooperative as the communal mill. In many of the villages, they still hold the *Foire de l'Ail* – the garlic fair which traditionally celebrates the most famous of France's ingredients. The restaurants offer sumptuous Provençal dishes which all have one thing in common – simplicity. From the *haute cuisine* to which we were treated to the café snacks, there was an emphasis on flavour and a blend of natural fresh products.

In the square in Uzès, where film actor Gerard Depardieu depicted Cyrano de Bergerac dashing away with those love letters, André Rogier cooks simple, delicious Provençal food at Myou restaurant.

La Marmite de Pecheur

This literally means the fisherman's stock pot. In Provence they would use local rockfish such as *rascasse, girelles* etc; choose instead from red mullet and snappers, lemon sole, whiting, cod, halibut etc.

SERVES 6

3 lb (1.4 kg) selected fish (see above)
4 tbsp extra virgin olive oil
2 medium onions, peeled and chopped
2 garlic cloves, peeled and chopped
a few sprigs of fennel, and some stalks
2 bay leaves
a pinch of saffron
salt and pepper

Clean the fish and cut into pieces.

Heat the oil in a large pan, add the onion and garlic, and sauté until soft. Add the fish, fennel, bay leaves, saffron and seasoning, and stir to mix and colour in the oil. Add 3 pints (1.7 litres) water and simmer for 15 minutes.

Push through a fine sieve lined with muslin to catch all the bones, etc. Pound the fish and bones well. Season the soup to taste, and serve hot with mussels.

Wine: A crisp Sauvignon Blanc or, more specifically, Touraine Sauvignon from the Loire valley.

Lamb with Pistou Sauce

SERVES 4

18 oz (500 g) fillet of lamb, cut into 1 inch (2.5 cm) slices

Pistou

2 oz (50 g) basil leaves
1 garlic clove, peeled
3–4 tbsp extra virgin olive oil

Pound the pistou ingredients in a mortar. Spread over the lamb slices and leave to marinate for up to 4 hours (or overnight) in the fridge.

Grill the lamb to taste, and serve with salad or vegetables.

Wine: A warm Southern French red from the Languedoc – Roussillon region or a newcomer from Corbières called Domaine du Reverend.

Marinated Sardines

It never ceases to amaze us how raw fish can be 'cooked' by a marinade alone, but we're assured that the acid in the lemon is the key element and, in that little square in Uzès, it tasted fantastic. Simple, cheap and highly nutritious, here's how it's done, to serve four.

Marinate 1 lb (450 g) sardine fillets in a mixture of 1 tbsp white wine vinegar, juice of 2 lemons, salt and pepper for 3–4 hours, covered with clingfilm in the fridge. Cover with extra virgin olive oil and serve with a salad.

Wine: Either any crisp dry white with lots of flavour and containing some Sauvignon Blanc or a Burgundy white – Bourgogne Aligoté

Alain Reymond

Alain Reymond is the award-winning chef at L'Auberge de St Hilaire de Brethams on the Route de Nîmes. Here are some of his favourite Provençal dishes that he prepared for us.

Saumon Mariné
au Citron Vert
et aux Epices
Salmon in Indian Spices

Alain explained that a lot of people in the South of France use spices in their cooking for the same reason as the Indian do – the heat. 'It seems strange to want to eat very hot food in intense temperatures, but by making the body sweat, the spices keep us cool.'

SERVES 4

1 lb (450 g) fresh salmon fillets, sliced thinly
sea salt

Marinade

1/4 tsp each of curry powder, turmeric, cardamom seeds,
*   cloves, cumin seeds*
juice of 2 limes
1 garlic clove, peeled and crushed
2 shallots, peeled and sliced finely
2½ fl oz (75 ml) dry white wine
5 fl oz (150 ml) extra virgin olive oil

Make the marinade up to 4–5 days before using. Crush the spices together in a mortar, then mix with the remaining ingredients. Cover and allow to develop flavour in the fridge.

Cover the salmon with sea salt and leave for 6 hours before preparing. Wipe clean.

Place the salmon in a dish and cover with the marinade. Leave for 2 days in the fridge.

Drain and serve with *fromage blanc*, lemon juice and chives.

Wine: Domaine Gournier Sauvignon.

Langoustines with Cognac

SERVES 6

24 large Dublin Bay prawn tails, shelled
4 tbsp extra virgin olive oil
1 lb (450 g) leeks, cleaned and cut into julienne strips
salt and pepper

Sauce

4 fl oz (120 ml) extra virgin olive oil
1 leek, sliced very thinly
2 shallots, peeled and sliced thinly
1 carrot, diced
½ tbsp herbes de Provence
1 tbsp tomato purée
3 tbsp Cognac
8 fl oz (250 ml) dry white wine

For the sauce, mix all the ingredients together with some seasoning in a saucepan, and simmer for 20 minutes. Sieve through muslin.

Cook the prawns in a frying pan with the olive oil, minutes only. Remove and keep warm. Fry the leek strips quickly in the same oil until soft. Season.

Place the prawns on top of the leeks and serve with the sauce.

Wine: Domaine Gournier Sauvignon.

Pruneaux au Vin Rouge

To serve six, soak 18 oz (500 g) prunes in cold water until swollen, then drain. Meanwhile, in a saucepan, mix together 15 fl oz (450 ml) red wine, 2 cloves, the roughly chopped rind of 1 orange, ½ cinnamon stick and 6 black peppercorns. Simmer for 1 hour to allow the alcohol to evaporate. Add the prunes and leave to simmer for a further 15 minutes. Cool, then refrigerate and serve with *fromage frais*.

Bruno Grifolle

Down the road at La Bregude St Pierre, Bruno Grifolle prepared an astonishing selection of imaginative vegetarian dishes. His presentation was that of an artist, but the ingredients were a clever fusion of texture and colour, yet not difficult to emulate. A raw cucumber soup was followed by a palate cleanser of melon, redcurrants, raspberries and figs before a salad of rocket, radish, two sizes of tomatoes, with oranges, green beans and red peppers. Cauliflower florets were marinated in orange juice and lemon, courgettes were served as spaghetti, and red peppers were oven-baked, seeded and blended to make a coulis. Some vegetables were cooked while other were raw; the flavour and colour of the dishes were breathtaking.

This was followed by a dish of celery hearts boiled and served with grapefruit and leek julienne in truffle juice but at £300 per kg from neighbouring Uzès, it might just be a little out of most people's league.

Next came an extraordinarily simple poached egg on a bed of chanterelle mushrooms with cracked wheat and chives in a reduced mushroom sauce.

Three sorbets served with peach, strawberries and raspberry coulis left us feeling totally satiated but not in the least bloated as might well be the case after a traditional six-course meal.

Most of Bruno's recipes are self-explanatory, except perhaps these two.

Raw Cucumber Soup

Grate ½ a large cucumber, which has been peeled and seeded, into a sieve or colander and sprinkle with salt. Leave to drain for at least 30 minutes. Rinse and blend with 2 tsp white wine vinegar, 1 tbsp extra virgin olive oil, ½ tsp Tabasco (or to taste) and 14 oz (400 g) plain yoghurt. Drop a rocket leaf in the bottom of each bowl, pour the soup in, and garnish with a slice of large red radish.

Wine: A light fresh dry white such as a Gaillac Blanc from the Midi or a Manzanilla Sherry.

Poached Egg with Wild Mushrooms

Per person, cover 1 oz (25 g) chanterelles with a little water and simmer for 5 minutes to cook and reduce. Add 2 tbsp chicken stock, some snipped chives and a handful of cracked wheat. Simmer until the wheat is soft, minutes only. Poach the egg in water with a drop of vinegar and some salt. Serve immediately.

Papetou D'Aubergines
Aubergine Flan with Tomato Coulis

Maurice and Catherine Barnouin also gave us some of
their own favourite Provençal recipes which they frequently cook at home. The tomato coulis which accompa-
nies the first dish is indispensable in Provençal cooking.

SERVES 4

2 medium aubergines
salt and pepper
6 tbsp olive oil
2 garlic cloves, peeled and crushed
3 shallots, peeled and sliced finely
a sprig of fresh thyme
1 bay leaf
4 eggs, beaten

Coulis de Tomates

2 tbsp extra virgin olive oil
3 garlic cloves, peeled and sliced thickly
2 sprigs of parsley
2 medium onions, peeled and chopped
about 18 oz (500 g) ripe tomatoes, skinned, seeded and
  chopped finely
salt and pepper
1 sprig of fresh thyme
1 bay leaf
1 tsp sugar

Peel the aubergines and cut into lengthwise strips. Sprinkle with salt and leave to drain, about an hour, then rinse
and dry. Put in a pan with the olive oil, garlic, shallots,
thyme and bay leaf and cook, covered, over a high flame.
When the aubergine is soft, remove the bay leaf and
thyme, and blend the aubergine mixture in a food processor, mixing in the beaten eggs.

Pour into a suitable dish, and poach in a bain-marie for 35 minutes.

Meanwhile, make the tomato coulis. Put a large pan over a high flame, add the oil, then throw in the garlic and parsley. Take out after 1 minute, using a slotted spoon. Add the onion, tomato, salt, pepper, thyme and bay leaf, and simmer for 1 hour. Add a little sugar if necessary, to relieve the acidity of the tomatoes.

Serve the aubergine flan cut into slices or wedges, with the tomato coulis.

Wine: A salmon pink Provence rosé or a red Minervois.

Soupe au Pistou

SERVES 8–12

*9 oz (250 g) each of dried haricot beans and red kidney
beans*
2 bouquets garnis
*11 oz (300 g) green beans, trimmed and chopped into ½
inch (1 cm) lengths*
5 large tomatoes, chopped finely
3 large potatoes, peeled and chopped finely
2 large carrots, chopped finely
4 large onions, peeled and chopped finely
4 medium courgettes, chopped coarsely
7 oz (200 g) short pasta

Pistou

about 2 oz (50 g) basil leaves
4 garlic cloves, peeled and chopped
*4 oz (100 g) Parmesan cheese, grated (or a mixture of
grated Gruyère and Edam)*
10 tbsp extra virgin olive oil
2–4 tbsp soup stock
1 tbsp tomato purée (optional, for taste)
salt and pepper

Soak the beans separately in plenty of cold water overnight. The next day, drain. Again separately, cover with
fresh water and bring to the boil. Boil for 10 minutes, then
add the bouquets garnis, and simmer for about 1 hour.
Discard the bouquets garnis. Drain the red beans and add
them to the pot with the white beans and their water.

Add the vegetables to the white bean pot, cover with
water, and leave to cook for 30 minutes, stirring from time
to time. Remove the courgettes, crush them and return to
the soup to add texture.

Add the pasta, and cook for a further 10 minutes, or until cooked.

Meanwhile make the pistou. Crush the basil, garlic and cheese together in a mortar. Add the olive oil, a bit at a time, and then stir in the stock and purée if used. Season, then pour into a pot and heat gently without boiling.

Either add the pistou to the soup, or serve it on the side.

Wine: A zippy fresh white – a Vin de Pays des Côtes de Gasgogne or a big, round and complex white – Lirac Blanc.

Anchoiade

This blend of anchovies and garlic can be the simplest or the most elegant of dishes to make. Spread on a piece of bread or toast it can be a delicious filler or canapé, while the addition of Cognac, pounded tomato and black olives can transform it into a perfect pâté or starter. Try this in-betweeny which Maurice and Catherine make for a lunch with friends.

SERVES 4–6

8 oz (225 g) anchovies in oil
4 garlic cloves, peeled
1 raw egg
a little black pepper
a dash of white wine vinegar
1-3 tbsp extra virgin olive oil

Purée all the ingredients in a blender, adding olive oil gradually until you get the right consistency.

Serve with fresh toast or bread, or with crudités like chunks of celery, artichoke hearts, carrots, cauliflower and fennel.

Wine: A full and dry Provence rosé would be excellent but a splendid choice would be Domaine Ott Château de Selle Rose. A Sauvignon Blanc is another option.

SPAIN

Maria José Sevilla, who presented the BBC programme *Spain on a Plate*, told us that the essence of the best Spanish cooking is simplicity. 'Dry roasted vegetables which are then drizzled with olive oil are very often the kinds of things people will prepare,' she said. 'And how difficult is it to put a load of peppers, courgettes, onions and potatoes in the oven?' She has written a number of cookery books about Spanish cooking, including one to accompany her BBC series, plus *Life and Food in the Basque Country*, and gave us some recipes from them.

Tortilla De Cebolla Y Bacalao
Salt Cod, Parsley and Onion Omelette

SERVES 2

2 tbsp olive oil
2 medium onions, peeled and sliced
9 oz (250 g) salt cod, desalinated (see page 187)
2 tbsp chopped parsley
4 eggs, beaten
salt

Put the oil in a casserole with the onion and sweat until golden-brown, then remove from the heat. Put a frying pan on the heat and transfer the contents of the casserole, including the oil, to it. Add the flaked cod and parsley, and leave to cook for a few minutes, stirring to prevent sticking. Finally, add the beaten egg, salt to taste, and cook. The omelette is turned over by means of a plate or folded in half, but in either case it should be quite runny in the middle.

Wine: Gran Viña Sol (Torres) – a very fresh choice.

Arroz Con Almejas
Baked Rice with Clams

SERVES 2

9 oz (250 g) short-grain rice
vegetable stock (see method)
1 tbsp olive oil
½ green pepper, finely sliced
1 garlic clove, peeled and chopped finely
9 oz (250 g) fresh clams
salt

Preheat the oven to 350°F (180°C) Gas 4. Measure the volume of the rice in a measuring jug, and use three times that of vegetable stock.

Put the oil in an earthenware or heavy-bottomed pan and add the green pepper, frying it until soft. Lightly brown the garlic, then add the rice and clams. Season with salt. Finally, pour over the measured stock, and bake for 20 minutes.

Wine: A Rioja rosé such as a full-boded dry produced by Marques de Cáceres, a new-style white Rioja or a Catalonian white from Penedés.

Merluza En Salsa Verde
Hake in Green Sauce

SERVES 6

olive oil
2 garlic cloves, peeled and sliced
2 lb (900 g) fresh hake, cut into thick slices
about 2 tbsp finely chopped parsley

Put the oil and garlic into a casserole and sauté gently.
Make sure the oil is not too hot, so that the garlic stews
rather than fries. When the garlic is golden, add the fish
and sprinkle with parsley. The heat should be low. After a
few minutes, the hake will begin to release a whitish
liquid. Shake the pan gently so that the sauce begins to
thicken, and the garlic and oil emulsify after about 15
minutes.

Wine: A quite delicate wine is needed – a Chardonnay or
         a Sauvignon Blanc.

Restaurants by Chefs

PHILIP OWEN
Arts Theatre Café

While sulking one day about having been let down for an appointment, we found ourselves standing outside The Arts Theatre Café near Leicester Square in London. Noticing that the menu represented the virtues of the Mediterranean Health Diet, we went in to meet its chef Philip Owens. During lunch we were extremely impressed with the variety and simplicity of the mostly vegetarian dishes. We have, therefore, devoted a larger proportion of the recipe section to these, all of which are inexpensive and full of fresh readily available ingredients. We think that his success will come from his down-to-earth approach to food.

'I've always been into healthy foods, and have never quite understood why people would want to eat out of a box when it takes less time and is much tastier, for instance, to prepare a quick tomato sauce. By the time you've cooked your pasta, you can have made a wonderful home-made sauce for a fraction of the price. Of course it pays to buy the best quality ingredients, especially if you're making the simpler foods where a sprig of fresh basil will add so much more taste than the dried version.

'I like strong flavours – I think that comes from not being formally trained as a chef and from following my own rules. I spent quite a few holidays in Sicily where I picked up an Arab influence of sweet and sour flavours. So I'll use pine nuts and raisins together in a dish with pomegranates and coriander, or sardines marinated in red onions and balsamic vinegar. I try to get away from the idea of meat being the centrepiece of a plate. My menu must be made up of about sixty per cent vegetarian dishes, but that's only because I find that there are so many wonderful things you can prepare them with.'

Broccoli and Cannellini Bean Soup

SERVES 4

12 oz (350 g) dried cannellini beans
6 tbsp extra virgin olive oil
2 garlic cloves, peeled and sliced thinly
½–1 dried red chilli, to taste
1 lb (450 g) broccoli, cut into tiny florets, with stalks sliced
    thinly
5 fl oz (150 ml) sieved tomatoes
1 pint (600 ml) chicken stock
1 tbsp chopped fresh oregano or marjoram
salt and pepper

Soak the beans overnight in plenty of cold water. The next day rinse well, cover with fresh water and bring to the boil. Simmer for 40–60 minutes until cooked, then drain.

Meanwhile, heat the oil in a large saucepan, and sauté the garlic for a minute or two. Add the dried chilli and broccoli. Sauté briefly, then add the sieved tomatoes and chicken stock, with the fresh herbs and drained beans. Simmer for 10 minutes – do not overcook. Add seasoning to taste.

Serve with *bruschetta* – toasted bread slices rubbed with crushed garlic and drizzled generously with olive oil – some more olive oil, and freshly grated Parmesan cheese.

Wine: Needs a red Rubesco to stand up to this dish.

Bread Soup, Tuscan Style

SERVES 4

3–4 tbsp extra virgin olive oil
2 medium leeks, trimmed, washed and sliced thinly
2 garlic cloves, peeled and sliced thinly
4 large plum tomatoes, sliced
15 fl oz (450 ml) chicken stock
4 slices of slightly stale white bread, crusts removed
sea salt and black pepper
1 oz (25 g) fresh basil leaves, shredded

Heat the olive oil in a large pan and sauté the leeks and garlic until soft – 10–12 minutes. Add the tomatoes and cook, stirring to soften them, for 25 minutes. Add the chicken stock and continue cooking for another 20 minutes. Cut the crustless bread into cubes, and add to the soup. Let stand for 10 minutes. Season to taste, then add the torn basil.

Serve with an extra drizzle of olive oil.

Wine: A robust red like Rubesco (Lungarotti) – Abbazia di Propezzano.

Lentil Soup

SERVES 4–6

1 lb (450 g) brown or green lentils
3 tbsp extra virgin olive oil
2 red onions, peeled and chopped finely
2 garlic cloves, peeled and sliced thinly
2 carrots, chopped finely
2 celery sticks, chopped finely
1 white part of leek, sliced thinly
1 oz (25 g) pancetta, diced
2½ pints (1.5 litres) chicken stock
salt and pepper
2 tbsp chopped fresh oregano and/or parsley

Pick over the lentils, then wash them well in a sieve under running water. Cover with water and leave overnight to soak. Drain well.

Heat the oil in a saucepan and gently cook the onion, garlic, carrots, celery, leek and *pancetta* until the vegetables are soft and the *pancetta* is brown. Add the lentils, and stir to mix so the lentils are well coated with oil. Add the chicken stock, and simmer for about 1 hour.

Season to taste with salt and pepper and add the chopped herbs. Pass through the thin disc of a mouli – you might have to do this twice depending upon the effectiveness of your mouli.

Taste again, and serve with a drizzle of extra olive oil, a sprig of fresh oregano and some *bruschetta* (see page 170).

Wine: Needs to be robust to stand up to this – a red Rubesco or a white Torre di Giano.

Orecchiette with Beetroot Tops, Anchovy, Garlic and Chilli

SERVES 4

Orecchiette (home-made pasta ears)

8 oz (200 g) semolina
1 lb (450 g) strong plain flour
8 fl oz (225 ml) cold water
½ tsp salt

Sauce

1 lb (450 g) beetroot tops, stalks removed (or turnip tops,
  or spinach)
3 tbsp extra virgin olive oil
2 garlic cloves, peeled and sliced thinly
2 anchovies
½–1 dried red chilli, to taste
3 plum tomatoes, skinned, seeded and chopped
freshly grated Parmesan cheese, to taste

Make the pasta 'ears' first. Blend the ingredients in a food processor for 2 minutes until a ball of dough is formed. Knead further by hand until the ball becomes elastic. Roll the dough into short cylinders of about ½ inch (2.5 cm) across, then cover with a damp cloth for 30 minutes. Cut into ½ inch (1 cm) discs. Flatten each disc with your thumb to make a little ear shape. Leave to dry, or use immediately. They take about 3–5 minutes to cook in boiling salted water, depending on the dryness of the pasta.

For the sauce, shred the vegetable leaves coarsely. Heat the oil in a large pan and sauté the garlic, anchovy, chilli and tomato. Add the shredded leaves, toss briefly so that the leaves 'fall' slightly, then add to the warm cooked pasta. Toss with Parmesan and serve immediately.

Wine: A robust red like Rubesco (Lungarotti) – Abbazia di Propezzano.

Spaghettini alla Caprese
Thin Spaghetti with Plum Tomatoes, Mozzarella, Basil and Black Olives

SERVES 4

1 lb (450 g) spaghettini
salt and pepper
1 tbsp freshly grated Parmesan cheese

Sauce

14 oz (400 g) plum tomatoes, skinned, seeded and diced
12 black olives, pitted and chopped
2 oz (50 g) fresh basil leaves, shredded
about 4 tbsp extra virgin olive oil
4 oz (100 g) Mozzarella (di Bufala, made from buffalo milk, if possible), diced finely

To make the sauce, mix the tomato dice with the chopped black olives and shredded basil. Toss with the olive oil. Add the diced Mozzarella and season with salt and pepper.

Cook the spaghettini according to packet instructions. Immediately toss with the raw sauce ingredients in a wok or large pan, adding the Parmesan. Place in warmed bowls, and serve immediately.

Wine: A light red because of the delicacy of the dish, served lightly chilled – Franciacorta Rosso (Bella Vista).

Pasta alla Norma
*Sicilian Pasta with Fruity Tomato Sauce
and Crispy Fried Aubergine*

SERVES 4

1 lb (450 g) spaghetti
salt and pepper
a handful of fresh basil leaves, shredded
*about 1 oz (25 g) strong Pecorino or Parmesan cheese,
  grated*

Fruity tomato sauce

2 lb (900 g) fresh ripe plum tomatoes
6 tbsp extra virgin olive oil
1 lb (450 g) onions, peeled and sliced thinly
2 large garlic cloves, peeled and sliced thinly

Crispy fried aubergine

1 medium aubergine
about 1 oz (25 g) plain flour
1 large egg, beaten
about 2 oz (50 g) fresh breadcrumbs
olive oil for shallow-frying

For the sauce, skin and seed the tomatoes, then chop coarsely. Heat the olive oil in a large pan and gently sauté the onion and garlic until soft. Add the tomato, cover, and gently reduce over a low heat until a thick paste is formed – at least 20 minutes. (You could simmer for up to 3 hours for a wonderful flavour, but you must take care the pan does not catch on the bottom.) Put the paste through a mouli, then season to taste.

For the aubergine, cut lengthwise in half, then slice into half-moon discs. Place in a colander and sprinkle with salt. Stand for 30 minutes, then dry well with kitchen paper.

Dip the aubergine discs first in flour, then in beaten egg, then the breadcrumbs.

Heat about an inch (2.5 cm) of oil in a large frying pan, and fry the breadcrumbed aubergine discs, a few at a time, until golden, minutes only. Drain well on absorbent paper, and keep warm.

Cook pasta according to instructions on the packet, drain, then toss with the fruity tomato sauce, the torn basil and cheese. Place in bowls with the crispy aubergine discs on top, and drizzle with extra virgin olive oil.

Wine: A robust red Rubesco, similar to Chianti.

Roasted Marinated Peppers

This basic method of roasting and skinning peppers can be used for numerous recipes.

SERVES 4
1 lb (450 g) peppers, red, green and yellow
2 garlic cloves, peeled and sliced thinly
1 tbsp drained capers
2 tbsp chopped parsley or coriander
a sprig of thyme
1 fl oz (25 ml) white wine vinegar
3 fl oz (85 ml) extra virgin olive oil
salt and pepper

Preheat the oven to 400°F (200°C) Gas 6.

Cut the peppers in half and remove white pith and seeds. Place pepper halves, skin down, on a baking tray and bake in the oven for about 30 minutes. Turn over and bake for a further 15 minutes. Remove from the oven and place in a bowl. Cover with clingfilm and leave for 10 minutes or so, by which time the skin should separate easily from the flesh. Cut each half pepper in half lengthwise (or into strips if you prefer).

Place in a dish and cover with the remaining ingredients, adding salt and pepper to taste. Marinate overnight. Serve cold.

Panzanella
Tuscan Bread Salad

SERVES 4

4 slices good quality white bread, cubed
8 tbsp extra virgin olive oil
4 large plum tomatoes, cubed
1 small cucumber, peeled and cubed
1 yellow pepper, seeded and white pith removed
2 tbsp chopped mixed fresh herbs (sage, basil, parsley,
  marjoram, oregano)
1/2 fennel bulb, sliced thinly and soaked in iced water
1 red onion, peeled, sliced thinly and soaked in iced water
1 celery stick, sliced thinly and soaked in iced water
salt and pepper
3 tsp each of balsamic and white wine vinegar
1 handful each of rocket and watercress leaves, shredded
4 anchovies
about 8 black olives

Preheat the oven to 400°F (200°C) Gas 6.

Drizzle the bread cubes with about half the olive oil, then bake on a tray in the oven for 10–15 minutes until golden. Drain well on absorbent paper.

In a large bowl, mix together the tomato, cucumber, pepper and chopped herbs. Drain and dry the fennel, red onion and celery, and add to the bowl. Season with salt and pepper, then dress with the remaining olive oil and the vinegars. Toss then, just before serving, mix in the croûtons, rocket and watercress, and garnish with anchovies and black olives.

Wine: Serve a slightly chilled red Franciacorta Rosso.

Pollo alla Diavola
Grilled Breast of Chicken

SERVES 4

4 chicken breasts, skinned and boned
6 tbsp lemon juice
at least 1 tbsp coarsely crushed black peppercorns
2 tbsp extra virgin olive oil
plenty of coarse sea salt

Misticanza

7 oz (200 g) mixed and prepared leaves (rocket, endive,
*   batavia, lamb's lettuce, radicchio, sorrel)*
2 tbsp chopped mixed fresh herbs (rosemary, sage, basil,
*   parsley)*
2 tbsp extra virgin olive oil
2 tsp each of balsamic and white wine vinegar

Cover the chicken breasts with clingfilm and beat flat. Arrange in a dish in one layer and coat with the lemon juice, crushed peppercorns and oil. Cover and leave to marinate for about 2 hours. Baste and turn occasionally.

When ready to cook, remove breasts from the marinade and coat with coarse sea salt. Grill on a hot cast-iron griddle or over charcoal for 8–10 minutes per side, basting with the marinade.

When cooked, sprinkle with more crushed pepper.

Serve with the *Misticanza* leaves and herbs – a country-style salad – tossed with the oil and vinegars and a little seasoning.

Wine: A red which is smoky, smooth and has lots of flavour – Aglianico del Vulture (D'Angelo).

Warm Duck Breast Salad with Savoy Cabbage, Red Cabbage and Pancetta

SERVES 4

4 duck breasts, skinned and boned
black peppercorns, coarsely ground
coarse sea salt
6 tbsp extra virgin olive oil
1 red onion, peeled and sliced thinly
6 juniper berries, crushed
½ Savoy cabbage, shredded
a little balsamic vinegar
salt and pepper
1 garlic clove, peeled and sliced thinly
2 oz (50 g) pancetta, cut into small strips
½ red cabbage, shredded
a handful of croûtons to garnish (see page 179)

Preheat the oven to 475°F (240°C) Gas 9.

Lay the breasts on a baking tray and season liberally with coarse pepper and salt. Roast in the hot oven for 15–20 minutes – they should still be pink. Remove from the oven, cover loosely, and leave to rest for 10 minutes before slicing thinly.

Heat half the olive oil in a pan, add the onion and juniper berries, and sauté briefly to soften the onion. Add the Savoy cabbage and toss for a moment or two over heat. Add a dash of balsamic vinegar, and season with salt and pepper. Remove from the heat and keep warm.

Heat the remaining olive oil and fry the garlic. Remove from the oil before it browns, and discard. Add the *pancetta* to the oil in the pan and fry until crispy. Remove and add the red cabbage, and toss for a moment or two over heat. Add a dash of balsamic vinegar, and season with salt and pepper. Keep warm.

Arrange the Savoy cabbage on one half of each warmed plate with the duck breast slices on top, and the red cabbage and crispy *pancetta* on the other half, with a scattering of croûtons.

Wine: A red – Aglianico del Vulture (D'Angelo).

Lamb Spiedini

SERVES 4

18 oz (500 g) lean lamb, minced
1 large red onion, peeled and minced finely
2 garlic cloves, peeled and minced finely
3 oz (75 g) mixed chopped fresh herbs (mint, rosemary,
  parsley, coriander)
salt and pepper

Combine all the ingredients and mix thoroughly, kneading the mixture. Fry or grill a small proportion of the mixture, taste, and adjust seasoning accordingly. Form the rest of the mixture into eight, twelve or sixteen patties (size to taste) and thread on to skewers. Grill, turning until evenly cooked.

Serve with Roasted Marinated Peppers (see page 178) and *bruschetta* (see page 170) or some good crusty Italian bread.

Wine: A well-flavoured red – Rubesco or Aglianico del Vulture.

Arista
Tuscan Roast Pork

SERVES 6

1 loin of pork, about 3½ lb (1.5 kg), boned, rolled
*   and tied*
5 lb (2.25 kg) pork bones
salt and pepper
about 10 fl oz (300 ml) white wine or chicken stock
*   (or a mixture)*

Marinade

2 tsp fennel seeds or 6 cloves
8 garlic cloves, peeled
6 sage leaves
leaves from 4 sprigs of fresh rosemary
2 tbsp extra virgin olive oil

For the marinade, grind the fennel seeds or cloves, garlic, herbs and oil together in a mortar. Slash the fat of the loin with a knife and press in the marinade. Cover loosely and leave to marinate overnight if possible.

When ready to cook, preheat the oven to 375°F (190°C) Gas 5. Place the bones in a large roasting tin, with the marinated loin on top. Season well with salt and pepper. Roast in the oven for about 2 hours, or until the meat is very tender, basting with a spoonful of the white wine or stock occasionally. Turn the oven up high – to at least 425°F (220°C) Gas 7 – for the last 15 minutes to crisp the crackling.

Remove the meat from the tin and keep warm. Pour off surplus fat from the tin and deglaze with the remaining wine or stock (or mixture). Boil to reduce to a gravy, and serve hot with the meat.

Wine: For simple dishes, a Tuscan wine with balance of acid and earthy – Rosso di Montalcino (Col d'Orcia) – or a dry Lambrusco to cut through the fattiness of the pork.

Salt Cod Fritters with Roasted Marinated Peppers and Rocket

SERVES 4

8 oz (225 g) salt cod
extra virgin olive oil
4 oz (100 g) rocket leaves, washed and dried
lemon juice
Roasted Marinated Peppers (see page 178)

Batter

6 tbsp plain flour
1 large egg, lightly beaten
5 fl oz (150 ml) low-fat milk
2 garlic cloves, peeled and crushed
1 tbsp chopped parsley
salt and pepper

Soak the cod in cold water for 24 hours, changing the water a couple of times. (This removes the salt.) Drain, rinse, and put in a pan with cold water to cover. Bring to the boil over a high heat, then drain, cool and dry well. Remove any skin and bones, and cut into small chunks (or flake the flesh).

To make the batter, put flour in a bowl and slowly mix in the beaten egg and milk until you have a smooth, thick mixture. Stir in the garlic and parsley, and add salt and pepper to taste.

Heat enough olive oil in a frying pan to come 1 inch (2.5 cm) up the sides. If using chunks of fish, dip them in the batter and fry in the hot oil until golden – about 5–10 minutes – turning once. If using flakes of fish, mix them into the batter and fry in spoonfuls for the same length of time. Drain well on kitchen paper.

To serve, on a large plate arrange the washed and dried rocket leaves. Dress them lightly with olive oil and lemon juice. Place the cod fritters in the middle, arranging the marinated peppers in between.

Wine: A white with good acidity – Gavi or Pigato.

Baked Trout with Fennel and Orange

SERVES 4

4 fresh trout, scaled and cleaned
1 large fennel bulb, sliced thinly
1½ oranges, sliced, with white pith and skin removed
2 sprigs of rosemary
salt and pepper
about 4 tbsp extra virgin olive oil
about 2 tbsp fresh orange juice

Preheat the oven to 400°F (200°C) Gas 6.

Make a layer of fennel and orange slices in a suitably sized earthenware dish. Place the trout and sprigs of rosemary on top. Season liberally. Drizzle with extra virgin olive oil and a squeeze of orange juice. Cover the dish with oiled foil, and bake in the oven for 15–20 minutes, depending on the size of the fish.

Wine: A fragant, flowery, elegant, full-flavoured Chardonnay – Francia Cortabianco (Bella Vista).

Baked Skate with Capers, Anchovy and Chilli

SERVES 4

*2½–3 lb (1–1.5 kg) skate wings, trimmed and cut into
    4 pieces*
2 tbsp capers, rinsed and soaked (if salted)
8 anchovies
3 green chillies, chopped (seeded if you prefer)
salt and pepper
4–5 tbsp extra virgin olive oil

Preheat the oven to 375°F (190°C) Gas 5.

    Place the skate pieces in an earthenware dish, and place
the capers, anchovies and chillies on top. Season to taste,
but go easy on the salt because of the anchovies. Drizzle
with the olive oil, cover with foil, and bake in the oven for
15–20 minutes.

    Serve with steamed broccoli and plenty of bread to soak
up the juices.

Wine: A robust, strong white wine – Torre di Giano
       (Lungarotti).

Stuffed Skewered Swordfish with Vegetables

SERVES 4

4 swordfish steaks, about 1 lb 5 oz (600 g) in total weight
5 fl oz (150 ml) extra virgin olive oil
salt and pepper
2 red onions, peeled and cut into chunks
4 plum tomatoes, thickly sliced
2 lemons, sliced thinly

Stuffing

2 oz (50 g) soft white or brown breadcrumbs
grated zest of ½ lemon
juice of ½ lemon
1 tsp capers, chopped
1 anchovy fillet, chopped
½ oz (15 g) Parmesan cheese, grated
1 tbsp chopped mixed fresh herbs (marjoram, basil, parsley)
1 garlic clove, peeled and crushed

Bone and skin the steaks if necessary. Cut through the steaks horizontally to make ½ inch (1 cm) slices. Cut these in half, and marinate in the olive oil for about 30 minutes before cooking.

Meanwhile combine all the ingredients for the stuffing, seasoning lightly with salt and pepper. Preheat the oven to 375°F (190°C) Gas 5.

Drain the swordfish well – keeping the oil – then season with salt and pepper. Place some of the stuffing on each piece and fold like a package, or roll up, depending on the size of the pieces. Thread on to skewers, alternating with chunks of red onion and slices of tomato and lemon.

Brush with the remaining olive oil marinade and bake in the oven for 15 minutes.

Wine: A rich white with good acidity – Pigato from Liguria.

Burrida
A Light Fish Stew with Crostini

SERVES 4

2 tbsp extra virgin olive oil
2 garlic cloves, peeled and sliced thinly
½–1 fresh green chilli, minced (optional)
5 fl oz (150 ml) sieved tomatoes
10 fl oz (300 ml) dry white wine
10 fl oz (300 ml) fish stock
2 tbsp chopped mixed fresh herbs (marjoram, basil, coriander)
1½ lb (700 g) assorted seafood, cleaned, prepared and cut into serving pieces (skate, cod, monkfish, mussels, squid)
salt and pepper

Crostini

8 slices French bread
2 garlic cloves, peeled and crushed
4 tbsp extra virgin olive oil

To make the *crostini*, preheat the oven to 400°F (200°C) Gas 6. Top the bread slices with crushed garlic, and a drizzle of olive oil. Bake until golden, about 15 minutes. Drain well on absorbent paper.

To make the broth, heat the oil in a large pan, and fry the garlic until just coloured. Add the chilli, if using, and the sieved tomatoes, and bring to the boil. Add the white wine, and boil to reduce a little. Add the stock and simmer gently for 20 minutes. Add the herbs and pieces of fish and poach for about 3–5 minutes. Taste and adjust seasoning.

Serve with the warm *crostini*.

Wine: A robust, acid and sharp white – Torre di Giano (Lungarotti) or Gavi.

Grilled Scallops and Squid with Rocket and an Orange, Green Chilli and Herb Dressing

SERVES 4

*8 fresh shelled scallops, sliced in half horizontally
  if large
12 oz (350 g) squid, cleaned and cut into strips
2 tbsp extra virgin olive oil
salt and pepper
6 oz (175 g) rocket leaves*

Dressing

*4 tbsp extra virgin olive oil
1 tbsp fresh orange juice
2 tsp balsamic vinegar
1/2–1 fresh green chilli, minced
1 tbsp chopped mixed fresh herbs (oregano, marjoram,
  coriander)*

Marinate the scallops and squid strips in the oil for a few minutes before cooking. Season lightly with salt and pepper.

Make the dressing by combining all the ingredients. Season to taste with salt and pepper.

Grill the squid strips for 2–3 minutes on both sides. Grill the scallops for 20 seconds each side. Toss both fish in the dressing.

Arrange the rocket leaves on individual plates, with the scallops and squid on top. Pour any remaining dressing over.

Wine: A white, acid, strong – Pigato.

Strawberries with Balsamic Vinegar

SERVES 4

2 punnets of strawberries
1 tbsp balsamic vinegar
caster sugar to taste (you might not need it)

Wipe the strawberries if necessary, then remove the stems. Place in a bowl with the vinegar (and sugar, if the strawberries are not sweet enough), and let stand for 1 hour before serving. Turn the strawberries occasionally.

Wine: A soft, simple, fruity Dolcetto d'Alba (Bersano).

Orange and Basil Sorbet

SERVES 8–10

10 oranges
2 lemons
10 oz (275 g) caster sugar
30 basil leaves, shredded

Remove rind from the washed and scrubbed fruit, making sure not to include any of the bitter white pith. Place chopped rind in a saucepan with the sugar and 1 pint (600 ml) water. Simmer until the sugar has dissolved, then boil until a syrup forms – about 5 minutes. Allow to cool.

Add the juice of the oranges and lemons, and the basil. Place in an ice-cream maker or *sorbetière* and freeze according to the manufacturer's instructions.

Wine: A light, delicate, sparkling wine with almonds – Prosecco (Gregoletto) – or a fruity, dry still white, Libaio (Ruffina).

Poached Plums with Honey and Rosemary

SERVES 4

16 plums, washed
10 fl oz (300 ml) dry white wine
4 tbsp honey
6 sprigs of fresh rosemary

Place all the ingredients in a saucepan, bring to the boil and simmer for 12–15 minutes. Allow to cool.

Serve simply with some Mascarpone, the Italian cream cheese.

Wine: An aromatic white – Castellaro Soave Classico (Bolla).

MARK JONES
The Angel Inn

Mark Jones at The Angel Inn at Long Crendon in Buckinghamshire is one of those untrained chefs who whips up a little number with the minimum fuss, creating a medley of textures, flavours and colours which would sell for big money in a less down-to-earth restaurant. He showed us a couple of recipes which can be made in less than ten minutes and which offer both a nutritional balance and are filling enough to provide a good lunch.

'Using fresh ingredients is the key to making a simple and relatively inexpensive meal which tastes great. With a much wider range of quality food in supermarkets these days, it's difficult to make a mistake if you keep it simple. I use a lot of different flavours in my oils which I make up myself. We're all used to making vinaigrette and this involves a fair amount of creativity; we might add a bit of honey or mustard for taste to a dressing, so why not apply that lateral thinking to oils and use them as marinades or as the final touch to a dish?'

Beef Carpaccio

This dish is best if the beef has been marinated in the chilli oil for some hours. Mark Jones makes his own chilli oil by dropping a couple of fresh or dried chillies into a bottle of extra virgin olive oil and leaving for up to a fortnight. (He uses Philip Berio's oil which is inexpensive and available in most supermarkets.) The chillies keep well in the oil, and give it some of their flavour and heat.

Per person
*about 4 oz (100 g) tail end of fillet steak, cut thinly into 2
    inch (5 cm) squares*
a little chilli olive oil (see above)
2 sun-dried tomatoes, drained of oil
*1/2 oz (15 g) fresh Parmesan cheese, scraped into curls
    (use a potato peeler)*
a few leaves of fresh basil, shredded

If you haven't marinated the meat, place the slices on a sheet of clingfilm, drizzle with a little chilli oil, and cover with another sheet of clingfilm. Bash the pieces gently to make them flat and very thin. Chill for the best flavour.

Arrange on a plate with the sun-dried tomatoes. Sprinkle with the curls of Parmesan and the basil, and serve.

Wine: An Australian Dalwood medium Chardonnay.

Baked Mushrooms in Chilli Oil and Tapenade

The tapenade, because of the preservative quality of the oil, can be kept in a fridge for a week if covered.

SERVES 4–6

8–12 large field mushrooms
a little chilli oil (see previous page)
a little crushed garlic
Roasted Red Peppers (see page 178), cut into strips
2 tbsp chopped fresh basil

Tapenade

5 oz (150 g) stoned black olives
8 anchovy fillets
2 oz (50 g) capers, drained
5 garlic cloves, peeled
4 fl oz (120 ml) olive oil
1 tbsp grated Parmesan cheese
salt and pepper

Make the tapenade first by simply mixing the ingredients together in a blender.

Preheat the oven to 350°F (180°C) Gas 4.

Lightly drizzle the mushrooms with oil and garlic, then bake for about 5 minutes until they have softened a little. Spread with the tapenade, and garnish with roasted red peppers and chopped basil.

Serve on a bed of salad, if you like.

Wine: An Australian Oxford Landing Chardonnay.

MADDALENA BONINO
Bertorelli's Restaurant

Maddalena Bonino is the chef at Covent Garden's Italian restaurant, Bertorelli's. Located opposite the Royal Opera House, her clientèle ranges from tourists to culture vultures with their varying tastes. Her trick is to make simple food look beautiful. She has been cooking in England for fifteen years, after coming here as an *au pair* at seventeen and using her full imagination to keep her charges happy in the kitchen. She has become used to customers sending warm salads back because they think that they should be cold, and refusing their tepid vegetables because they think that they should be piping hot.

With the kind of patience that marks the true foodie, she is continually creating new dishes for her customers. Nutrition is always uppermost in her mind although, she says, it's important not to preach. She believes that restaurants such as Bertorelli's where healthy food is always available, are subconsciously changing the food agenda. She's also been interested in food as a cure since her father suffered from diabetes.

'A lot is being written about food: what we should eat, what we should avoid, how much, when, how often . . . I would suggest one simple rule – eat as great a variety of foods as possible and enjoy yourself while doing it! We often eat for the wrong reasons or attach to food the wrong responsibilities. I started cooking while still rather young, and became aware of the "power" of food through my father's diabetic diet. Still, in spite of what may sometimes be limitations, food should be fun and not a punishment. I come from a tradition where food is always seen as a social occasion: buying, cooking and eating it. True, this may be the norm in the rural Italian countryside and less likely while leading a busy life in a British city, but the ingredients can now be found here and the pleasure of sharing a meal with family and friends should be sampled by everybody.'

Maddalena is the author of *The Festive Food of Italy*.

Pumpkin Risotto

SERVES 6

2½ pints (1.5 litres) chicken or vegetable stock
1 tbsp olive oil
1 medium onion, peeled and chopped
1½ lb (700 g) pumpkin flesh, chopped
1 lb (450 g) Arborio rice
5 fl oz (150 ml) dry white wine
4 oz (100 g) Parmesan cheese, grated
½ small chilli seeded and finely chopped
4 oz (100 g) whole almonds, roasted and chopped finely
salt and pepper

Heat the stock. In a frying pan, heat the oil, and gently fry the onion and pumpkin until lightly coloured. Add the rice and cook dry for a few minutes. Add the white wine and keep stirring until it has evaporated. Add the hot stock, a few ladles at a time, stirring continuously. Allow stock to be absorbed between additions. This will take up to 20–30 minutes, depending on how well cooked you like your rice. When the rice is ready, add the Parmesan, chilli and almonds. Season, remove from heat and stir. Leave to stand for 5 minutes before serving.

Wine: A medium Sauvignon or a top range Borro della Sala.

Asparagus Gratin with Parmesan and Herbs

SERVES 4

2 lb (900 g) asparagus, peeled and trimmed
6 oz (150 g) Parmesan cheese, grated
2 tbsp chopped fresh basil
2 tbsp chopped fresh mint
salt and pepper

Preheat the oven to 400°F (200°C) Gas 6.

Bring a large pot of salted water to the boil and cook the asparagus until just tender. Drain and refresh in cold water.

Arrange the asparagus in a greased ovenproof dish in no more than three layers, sprinkling each layer with Parmesan, basil, mint and black pepper. Bake in the oven for 15–20 minutes or until golden.

Wine: Fetzer Sundial or a medium Tuscany colti buono bianco.

Baked Monkfish with Roast Plum Tomatoes and Black Olive Dressing

SERVES 6

5 tbsp olive oil
3 garlic cloves, peeled and crushed
2 sprigs of fresh oregano
9 firm plum tomatoes, whole
salt and pepper
6 × 6 oz (175 g) monkfish fillets
3 lemons

Dressing

7 oz (200 g) pitted black olives
1 small bunch of flat-leaf parsley
1 garlic clove, peeled
7 fl oz (200 ml) olive oil
finely grated zest of 2 lemons

Preheat the oven to 425°F (220°C) Gas 7.

Make the dressing by mixing all the ingredients in a blender. Keep to one side.

Heat 3 tbsp of the oil in an ovenproof dish, and add the crushed garlic, oregano, then the whole plum tomatoes. Season with salt and crushed black pepper. Bake in the oven for about 15 minutes. Remove from the oven, cut each tomato in half, and keep warm.

Heat the remaining oil in a frying pan until very hot, and sear the monkfish fillets to colour on both sides. Turn the heat down, season, and simmer for about 15 minutes until cooked.

When the fish is ready, arrange on a plate, decorate with the tomato halves, and drizzle some of the tomatoes' juice over the dish.

Serve with the olive dressing and lemon segments.

Wine: Isistri from Tuscany, or a Chardonnay.

Steamed Skate on Leek Noodles with Spicy Aïoli

SERVES 6
2 leeks
2½ lb (1 kg) skate fillets, skinned
a little olive oil
salt and pepper
3 lemons
1 tbsp chopped flat-leaf parsley

Spicy aïoli

2 egg yolks
1 small green chilli, seeded
1 tbsp plain mustard
a few basil leaves
a small piece of fresh root ginger
a small piece of lemongrass
1 tbsp balsamic vinegar
2 tbsp white wine vinegar
3 garlic cloves, peeled
1 pint (600 ml) olive oil

For the aïoli, put all the ingredients in a blender except for
the oil, and process until smooth. Gradually add the oil
and whizz until the mixture is creamy. Season with salt
and pepper and keep in the fridge.

Trim the leeks, cut in half crosswise, then in half
lengthwise. Take a few layers of leeks at a time and cut
into long thin noodles. When they're all ready, wash and
drain well.

Cut the skate fillets in three following the fibres of the
fish. Arrange fish and leeks in a steamer, lightly brush
with a little oil and season. Steam for about 10 minutes.

Arrange the cooked fish on a serving plate, decorate

with leeks and lemon wedges, and sprinkle with the
chopped parsley.

Serve with the spicy aïoli and plain boiled potatoes

Wine: A fruity red such as the Californian Chardonnay
Firestone or Chianti Ruffini.

Roast Breast of Chicken with a Pepper and Caper Salsa

SERVES 6

3 tbsp olive oil
6 chicken breasts, about 7 oz (200 g) each,
  preferably maize-fed
salt and pepper
3 lemons

Salsa

1 red and 1 yellow pepper, cleaned and diced finely
1 small red onion, peeled and diced finely
2 spring onions, diced finely
1 small fresh green chilli, seeded and chopped finely
2 tbsp capers, chopped finely
3 tbsp finely chopped flat-leaf parsley
juice of 1 lemon
3 tbsp extra virgin olive oil

Preheat the oven to 450°F (230°C) Gas 8.

For the salsa, mix all the ingredients together and adjust the seasoning. Keep in a cool place to marinate for about an hour.

Heat the oil in a frying pan, and sauté the chicken breasts on both sides. Transfer to a heated roasting tin, season and roast in the oven for about 15–20 minutes, turning from time to time.

Serve the chicken with the salsa and lemon segments, and drizzle with a little extra virgin olive oil if required.

Wine: A medium dry light red such as Barbera d'Alba or
a Chianti classico.

ANDY MAGSON
Café Fish

Andy Magson is the senior chef at Café Fish in London's Theatreland. He uses many French recipes which, he says, tend to fox the British public when they think about cooking fish at home. 'I've always wondered why fish has never become more popular in the household, especially as we live on an island with some of the best fish in the world. Fish and chips is seen by foreigners as British food, but most British people are terrified of the fish itself. It's really important to have a good rapport with your fishmonger – and many supermarkets have them now. A good fishmonger will fillet and prepare your fish so all you have to do is pop it in the oven with some herbs. He or she will also advise you on the best choice for your budget.'

Troncon de Lotte Rôti à la Petie Ratatouille
Roasted Monkfish with a Fine Ratatouille

SERVES 4

1 × 3 lb (1.4 kg) monkfish tail
2 tsp fresh thyme leaves
salt and pepper

Ratatouille

4 tbsp olive oil
½ medium onion, peeled and sliced finely
¼ fennel bulb, sliced finely
1 medium courgette, cut into thin strips
½ medium aubergine, cut into thin strips
1 clove garlic, peeled and crushed
1 tbsp tomato purée
½ each of medium red and green pepper, blanched, skinned and cut into thin strips
8 oz (225 g) tomatoes, skinned, seeded and cut into thin strips
2 fl oz (50 ml) white wine
1 tbsp Pernod
5 fl oz (150 ml) water
4 basil leaves, shredded

Preheat the oven to 400°F (200°C) Gas 6.

Remove black outer skin from the fish, trim any dark patches and remove any bones, top and bottom. Slice the tail across into twelve even pieces, each weighing about 3 oz (75 g).

To make the ratatouille, in a thick-bottomed pan, heat half the oil, and add the onion and fennel. Stir quickly. Add the courgette, aubergine and garlic, and cook for 2 minutes. Add the tomato purée and the pepper and tomato strips, and cook for a further 2 minutes. Pour in the white wine and Pernod and bring to the boil. Add the water, cook for a few minutes, and finish with the shredded basil. Season to taste.

Season the monkfish steaks and sprinkle with thyme leaves. Seal in a separate pan in the remaining oil, then roast quickly in the oven for 4–5 minutes. Take out of the oven and transfer the steaks on to the ratatouille. Continue cooking for a further 4–5 minutes. Serve immediately with saffron rice.

Wine: A rosé from Provence such as Maître Vignerons de St Tropez.

Vapeurette de Cabillaud aux Fines Herbes, Vinaigrette de Legumes

Steamed Fillet of Cod with Fresh Herbs and Warm Vegetable Vinaigrette

SERVES 4

4 × 6 oz (175 g) cod fillets
1 lb (450 g) leeks, cut into 1 × ½ inch (2.5 × 1 cm)
   strips
salt and pepper
1 tbsp fresh mixed chopped herbs (chives, parsley,
   tarragon, dill)

Vinaigrette

1 medium carrot, peeled and diced finely
3 celery sticks, stringed and diced finely
1 medium courgette, trimmed and diced finely
6 fl oz (175 ml) fresh carrot juice
1 tbsp white wine vinegar
4 fl oz (120 ml) extra virgin olive oil

Skin the cod fillets. Fold the tail ends under the fillets to form a parcel shape. Wash the leek well, then blanch in boiling salted water. Drain well.

For the vinaigrette, blanch all the vegetable dice lightly together in boiling salted water. Drain well. Warm the fresh carrot juice, then add the vinegar. Add the oil slowly, whisking continuously. Season, and add the diced vegetables.

Season the cod fillets, sprinkle with fresh herbs, and steam for 5–6 minutes, depending on the thickness of the cod.

Arrange the leeks in the centre of a warm plate. Lay the

cod fillets on top and spoon the warm vinaigrette around the outside.

Serve with fresh seasonal vegetables.

Wine: A light rosé from Provence such as Bandol.

Brochette de Fruits de Mer au Couscous, Sauce Tomate Epice
Charcoal-grilled Skewer of Seafood with Couscous and Spiced Tomato Sauce

The choice of fish is optional – use as cheap or expensive as you like or can afford. The best is a mixture of salmon, monkfish, gurnard, brill, shark and grey mullet.

SERVES 4

about 2 lb (900 g) fillets of mixed fish (see above) cut into ½ inch (1 cm) cubes
½ each of medium red and green peppers, cut into ½ inch (1 cm) chunks
½ medium onion, peeled and cut into ½ inch (1 cm) chunks
3 fl oz (85 ml) olive oil
1 garlic clove, peeled
juice of ½ lemon
1 bouquet garni
8 oz (225 g) couscous
15 fl oz (450 ml) vegetable stock
salt and pepper

Sauce

1 tbsp olive oil
½ medium onion, peeled and diced
½ each of medium red and green peppers, diced
4 fresh green chillies, seeded and diced
1 tbsp tomato purée
1 pinch each of paprika and chilli powder
8 oz (225 g) tomatoes, skinned, seeded and diced

Alternate the diced fish with a piece of pepper and onion on kebab skewers. Marinate the skewers in the olive oil with the garlic, lemon juice and bouquet garni for 3 hours.

For the sauce, heat the olive oil in a thick-bottomed pan. Add the diced onion, pepper, and chilli and fry for 3–4 minutes. Add the tomato purée, paprika and chilli powder, and cook for 1 minute. Add the diced tomato, and cook for a further 10 minutes or until soft. Moisten with a little water if required. Season to taste.

Wash the couscous well in plenty of cold water, then soak for 10 minutes. Drain well, making sure the grains have separated. Bring the vegetable stock to the boil. Set the steamer on top of the stock pan, and lay a piece of muslin on the bottom of the steamer. Sprinkle the couscous on top, cover and cook for 7–10 minutes. Stir the couscous gently with a fork to make sure the grains are separate and fluffy. Mix in a little extra olive oil and some seasoning.

Charcoal-grill the seasoned fish skewers, cooking on all sides for about 10 minutes. Arrange the fish in the middle of a warm plate, having removed the skewers. Garnish with the cooked couscous on one side and the spicy tomato sauce on the other.

Wine: A dry white from Spain such as Gran Viña Sol.

Truite en Papillote Citronée
Paper Envelope of Boned Trout
with Lemongrass

SERVES 4

4 × 14 oz (400 g) fresh river trout, filleted
1 medium carrot, peeled and cut into thin strips
1 leek, cut into thin strips
¼ medium head of celeriac, peeled and cut into
  thin strips
salt and pepper
4 sticks of lemongrass
2 tbsp olive oil
2 fl oz (50 ml) white wine
4 fl oz (120 ml) fish stock
½ egg white

Preheat the oven to 375°F (190°C) Gas 5.

Be sure to remove *all* the bones from the fillets. Cook the vegetable strips in boiling salted water for 2 minutes, then refresh in cold or iced water. Chop three of the sticks of lemongrass, just cover with water, and boil for 4–5 minutes or until well infused.

Fold four sheets of greaseproof paper in half, and brush with a little of the oil. Lay two seasoned trout fillets on the bottom half of each piece of paper, allowing a 1 inch (2.5 cm) gap to the edge. Arrange the vegetable spaghetti on top of the fillets, and pour in 1 dessertspoon of the lemongrass reduction. Sprinkle with white wine and a little fish stock. Garnish each trout with a ¼ piece of the remaining fresh lemongrass on the top.

Brush the edges of the greaseproof paper with egg white, fold over the top and press the edges together. Fold the outer edges a ½ inch (1 cm) inwards towards the trout to form a sealed paper bag. Brush the top of the bag with a little more oil and bake in the preheated oven for 15 minutes. During the cooking time, the bag will puff up and brown slightly.

Serve the trout in the paper bag immediately, opening the top at the last minute. Serve with seasonal vegetables.

Wine: An Italian light white such as Colla Vini.

Moules Marinières
Mussels Steamed with Herbs, Garlic and White Wine

SERVES 4

4½ lb (1.8 kg) fresh mussels
1½ fl oz (40 ml) olive oil
1 garlic clove, peeled and crushed
2 tbsp chopped fresh parsley and tarragon leaves
6 fl oz (175 ml) white wine
12 fl oz (350 ml) fish stock
1 medium shallot, peeled and finely chopped
salt and pepper

Scrub and beard mussels, making sure the shells are well scraped. Wash two or three times in fresh water. Throw away any that do not close when tapped: they are dead.

Heat a thick-bottomed pan for a minute, then add the mussels along with all the other ingredients and some seasoning. Place a tight-fitting lid on top and steam for 3–4 minutes over a high heat, or until the mussels have opened. Throw away any that have remained closed.

Transfer to bowls and serve immediately, with fresh baked French bread to mop up the juices.

Wine: A sharp white such as Entre-Deux-Mers from Grasse.

TONY HOWARTH
Soho Soho

Tony Howarth is the chef at Soho Soho, London's first restaurant where the menu is based on the Mediterranean Diet. Its owner, Lawrence Isaacson's testimony to how he lost weight and reduced a dangerously high cholesterol level is in Chapter 6.

Focaccia Di Avocado
E Parmesan
Toasted Italian Bread
with Avocado and Parmesan

SERVES 4

1 lb (450 g) flour
sea salt
9 fl oz (275 ml) warm water
1 oz (25 g) dried yeast
2½ fl oz (75 ml) olive oil
1 sprig of rosemary, chopped

Topping

2 avocados
12 anchovy fillets
4 oz (100 g) fresh young Parmesan, cheese in the piece
4 tbsp virgin olive oil
milled black pepper

For the bread, mix the flour and 1 tsp salt together in a bowl and make a well in the centre. Mix half the water with the yeast and leave until it becomes frothy. Add, along with the rest of the water, 4 tbsp of oil and the chopped rosemary, to the well in the flour. Mix well, then knead this mixture for about 15 minutes until it becomes soft and elastic. (If it becomes tight, add a little extra water.) Put into a large bowl, cover with clingfilm, and leave in a warm place for 1 hour until it doubles in volume.

Pre-heat the oven to 400°F (200°C) Gas 6.

When the dough is ready, tip it on to the table and roll it out until about ¼ inch (5 mm) thick. Place it on a baking sheet and brush with the rest of the oil. Then, as if you were playing the piano, make lots of finger indentations all over the pastry and sprinkle with sea salt. Leave the dough to rise for about another half hour, and then bake in the preheated oven for 20 minutes. When cooked, cut into four rectangles with a sharp knife.

For the topping, cut the avocado in half, remove and discard the stone, and peel. Slice each half thinly, and fan out on each piece of bread. Place the anchovy fillets over the top. Warm in the oven for 10 minutes. Remove and arrange on plates. With a potato peeler, shave the Parmesan over the avocado. Drizzle on some of the virgin oil, sprinkle with black pepper, and serve.

Wine: White, not too dry, such as Pouilly.

Pan-seared Aubergine and Courgette

SERVES 4

2 aubergines
4 courgettes
salt and pepper
2½ oz (60 g) red onions, peeled and chopped
2 garlic cloves, peeled and crushed
2 oz (50 g) each of black and green stoned olives,
  chopped roughly
1 tbsp drained capers, chopped
5 fl oz (150 ml) olive oil

Cut the vegetables into slices lengthwise about ¼ inch (5 mm) thick. Sprinkle the aubergines with salt and leave for the bitter juices to drain out. Rinse and dry.

Heat a thick-bottomed pan until it is smoking, and put the pieces of vegetables in the pan, one at a time, until each piece goes a dark colour. Remove and keep warm.

Let the pan cool a little, then add the chopped onion, garlic, olives, capers, and the oil. Toss until warm, and season with salt and pepper.

Lay a slice of aubergine, then a slice of courgette, across the plate, and dress with the olive mixture.

Wine: Pouilly or a light beaujolais such as St Amour.

Tomates au Four
Baked Plum Tomatoes

SERVES 4

2 lb (900 g) plum tomatoes, skinned and sliced
1 red and 1 green pepper, skinned and cut into strips
sea salt and freshly ground black pepper
1 bunch of fresh basil, shredded
2 oz (50 g) capers, drained and chopped
2 oz (50 g) fresh breadcrumbs
5 fl oz (150 ml) extra virgin olive oil
1 tbsp chopped fresh parsley
3 garlic cloves, peeled and crushed

Preheat the oven to 350°F (180°C) Gas 4.

Using an ovenproof dish, make a layer of tomatoes and sliced peppers. Season and add another layer of tomatoes, then the basil and capers. Season again, and add a final layer of tomatoes. Sprinkle with the breadcrumbs tossed with the oil, garlic and parsley. Bake in the preheated oven for 20 minutes, then leave to cool before serving.

Saumon aux Dix Secondes
Fillets of Scottish Salmon with a Basil Mayonnaise

SERVES 4

1 carrot, peeled
¼ mooli (white radish), peeled
1 leek, trimmed
2 oz (50 g) mange-touts, topped and tailed
1 red pepper, seeded
5 fl oz (150 ml) virgin olive oil
1 bay leaf
6 whole black peppercorns
1 garlic clove, peeled
1 bunch of fresh basil, shredded finely
4 fl oz (120 ml) low-fat mayonnaise
1 lb (450 g) salmon fillet, skinned,
*   with pin bones taken out*
sea salt and black pepper

Cut all the vegetables into very thin strips, like short
boot-laces. Place in a pan and add the oil, bay leaf,
peppercorns and garlic. Bring to the boil and remove from
the heat immediately. Leave to cool.

Add the basil to the mayonnaise.

Thinly slice the salmon as if it were smoked.

Warm the vegetables again and pile on to the centre of a
plate, using a slotted spoon. Arrange the salmon slices
over the top, making sure they do not overlap. Grind
fresh black pepper over them, grill until the salmon goes
opaque. Drizzle with olive oil from the vegetable pan,
sprinkle with sea salt and serve with the basil mayonnaise.

Wine: Pouilly.

Homard de Soleil
Lobster Salad

SERVES 4

4 × 1 lb (450 g) lobsters, cooked
1 frisée lettuce, washed and dried
4 oz (100 g) snow peas, topped, tailed and cut into strips
8 oz (225 g) thin asparagus, cooked
2 oz (50 g) shallots, peeled and chopped

Dressing

1 carrot, peeled and diced finely
1 leek, trimmed, halved and sliced thinly
1 courgette, diced finely
1 red and 1 green pepper, seeded and diced finely
1 fresh red chilli, seeded and diced finely
4 shallots, peeled and diced finely
2 garlic cloves, peeled and crushed
2½ fl oz (75 ml) walnut oil
¾ fl oz (20 ml) white wine vinegar
½ tsp ground star anise
2 tsp tomato purée
salt and pepper

For the dressing, mix all the diced vegetables with the other ingredients. Season to taste.

Take the lobster flesh out of its shells, and dice. Keep the claws intact. In a bowl, toss the diced lobster with the frisée leaves, snow peas, asparagus and shallot.

Arrange the lobster in the centre of four plates, then spoon the prepared dressing around the salad. To finish, lay the two claws on top of each salad.

Wine: Champagne.

DAVID ROWLES
Bar Gansa

Bar Gansa was one of the first tapas bars to appear in London. In fact the food is more correctly called *raziones*, which means that there is more on your plate than a few olives and peppers in oil. *Tapas* literally means lids, and refers to the little plates of food Spanish bartenders put over glasses to prevent the flies getting in. In Spain, the evening promenade will often take in a visit to a few tapas bars.

David Rowles is owner and chef here and comes from the West Country. His Spanish waiters insist though that he makes the most authentic tortilla 'this side of Valencia'. But he complains that he finds it difficult to find the vegetables in this country which make all the difference in a real Spanish dish. 'Tomatoes don't taste of anything, peppers are too perfectly shaped and devoid of flavour, and so I really have to shop around.' He used to be more aware of presentation when he was the chef at the Egon Ronay-awarded One Legged Goose in Primrose Hill, but now prefers putting everything into a pan of cumin-flavoured oil. 'The Spanish don't like to complicate things, and will always find the easiest way to do things. If skinning garlic they fry this in oil until the skins pop off. And peppers will be grilled, then thrown into a bowl of cold water where the skins will just fall off. You can learn a lot from a Mediterranean chef.'

Ensalada Bar Gansa
Roasted Radicchio Salad with Manchego Cheese and Serrano Ham

SERVES 4–6

5 × heads of radicchio, washed and cut into quarters
15 garlic cloves, peeled
4 fl oz (120 ml) olive oil
8 fl oz (250 ml) low-fat mayonnaise
9 oz (250 g) spinach leaves, washed and dried
9 oz (250 g) Manchego cheese, grated
9 oz (250 g) Serrano ham, cut into julienne strips (or prosciutto)

Preheat the oven to 350°F (180°C) Gas 4.

Put the radicchio and 12 of the garlic cloves into a baking dish in one layer, and cover with the oil. Bake for 30 minutes, then cool and chill for 1 hour.

Make a garlic mayonnaise (aïoli), by mixing together the mayonnaise and the remaining garlic, crushed. (Or make your own.)

To serve, place the radicchio on the spinach leaves on individual plates. Sprinkle with the grated cheese and julienne of ham. Encircle the radicchio with the garlic mayonnaise.

Wine: A Chardonnay such as Viñas del Vero 1990.

Ensalada de Verduras
Vegetable Salad

SERVES 6–8

3¼ lb (1.4 kg) aubergines
salt and pepper
2 red and 2 green peppers, seeded and quartered
18 oz (500 g) flat or field mushrooms, trimmed
2½ lb (1 kg) broccoli, cut into florets
5 corn-on-the-cobs, trimmed and kernels removed
2½ lb (1 kg) courgettes, sliced coarsely
2 bunches of spring onions, trimmed
4 fl oz (120 ml) extra virgin olive oil
1 bunch of fresh basil, shredded

Preheat the oven to 400°F (200°C) Gas 6.

Slice the aubergine lengthwise and sprinkle with salt.
Leave for at least 20 minutes, then wash and dry. Bake in
the oven for 20–30 minutes; bake the peppers as described
on page 178, then skin. Bake the mushrooms for 3–5
minutes.

Bring 5¼ pints (3 litres) of water to the boil. Cook the
broccoli and corn kernels for 1 minute, the courgette for
30 seconds. Drain well.

Put all the vegetables plus the spring onions into a bowl.
Mix with the olive oil, seasoning and fresh basil leaves.
Chill for 2 hours before serving.

Wine: A dry rosé such as Torres Cabernet Sauvignon
1990 from Chile.

Bonito y Lentejas con Salsa Tomate
Bonito Tuna with Lentil and Tomato Salsa

SERVES 4

2½ lb (1 kg) bonito tuna fillet
2 tbsp black peppercorns, ground coarsely
9 oz (250 g) green or brown lentils, soaked for 30 minutes
3 medium plum tomatoes, skinned and seeded
4 fl oz (120 ml) olive oil mixed with 1 tsp chopped fresh chillies
a handful of mixed salad leaves

Cut the tuna into ½ inch (1 cm) thick steaks, or ask your fishmonger to do it for you. Coat the steaks with cracked peppercorns.

Cook the lentils for 15 minutes in fresh boiling water, then drain. Cut the tomatoes into tiny dice. Mix the lentils and tomato dice together and add the majority of the chillied oil.

Fry the tuna steaks in the remaining hot oil for 45 seconds on each side.

Arrange the mixture of tomatoes and lentils on a mixed leaf salad on individual plates, and top with the tuna.

Wine: Gran Viña Sol.

Gazpacho Andaluz
Chilled Tomato and Pepper Soup

SERVES 6

5 lb (2.25 kg) tomatoes, skinned and seeded
1 garlic clove, peeled
about 4 tbsp olive oil
1 large red and 1 large green pepper, seeded and chopped
1 cucumber, peeled and chopped
5 fl oz (150 ml) wine vinegar

Blend the tomatoes with the garlic and about half the olive oil. Blend the chopped peppers with the remaining oil. Blend the cucumber with the wine vinegar. Mix the three mixtures together, and blend once again, then chill for at least 4 hours.

Garnish with croûtons, diced pepper, diced cucumber and chopped spring onion.

PREM KUMAR
St James Court Hotel

Prem Kumar began his culinary career as a medical student, and knows a fair bit about nutrition as a result. His childhood in India also taught him about the medicinal qualities of herbs. He learned to cook in France and the result is a combination of Indian, French and nutrition-conscious cooking at St James Court Hotel, just behind Buckingham Palace.

Teen Dhung Ki Paneer
Three-Colour Paneer

SERVES 4

12 oz (350 g) paneer (an Indian cheese)
1 pint (600 ml) plain yoghurt
1 tsp chilli powder
1½ tsp garam masala
1 tbsp garlic paste
a pinch of saffron strands
3 tbsp lemon juice
2 tbsp green chilli paste
2 tbsp chopped fresh mint
2 tbsp chopped fresh coriander
1 tbsp almond purée
1 tbsp almond powder
1 tbsp ginger paste
seeds from 6 cardamon pods, ground
salt

Cut the paneer into 24 cubes of even size. Divide into three portions.

For the saffron paneer, in a bowl mix a third of the yoghurt with 1 tsp each of the chilli powder and garam masala, and the garlic paste. Boil the saffron in 4 fl oz (120 ml) water. Drain and add the soaked strands to the mixture. Add 1 tbsp of the lemon juice, mix, then place the paneer in the marinade and marinate for a day.

For the mint paneer, mix half of the remaining yoghurt with half the green chilli paste, the mint, coriander, almond purée, 1 tbsp of the lemon juice, and a pinch of garam masala. Marinate the paneer in the mix for a day.

For the cardamom paneer, mix the remaining yoghurt with the almond powder, ginger paste, remaining green chilli paste, ground cardamom, salt and remaining lemon juice, and marinate the paneer as above.

Before serving, place the three paneers separately on an

oiled tray in a hot oven – 400°F (200°C) Gas 6 – for 15–20 minutes. Serve on a bed of salad with the two chutneys below.

Wine: Omar Khayyam – Méthode Champenoise or Gran Viña Sol.

Mint Chutney

1 bunch of fresh mint
½ bunch fresh coriander
8 fl oz (250 ml) plain yoghurt
1 tsp grated fresh root ginger
2 fresh green chillies
salt
lemon juice

Put the first five ingredients in a blender, and process to a fine purée. Add salt and lemon juice to taste.

Aam Ki Chutney

½ packet tamarind
8 fl oz (250 ml) water
2 tsp aniseed
1 tsp red chilli powder
2 oz (50 g) fresh dates
black pepper
2 oz (50 g) jaggery (or brown sugar)
4 black cardamoms, lightly crushed

Put all the ingredients in a saucepan and bring to the boil. Cook on a slow heat for 15 minutes. Pass through a sieve.

Tursi aur Anaar Dana ki Macchi
Halibut with Basil and Pomegranate Seeds

SERVES 2

2 halibut pieces, 6 oz (175 g) each, skinned and boned
1 tsp ground coriander
1 tbsp garlic paste
1 tsp chopped green chilli
salt
1 tsp pomegranate seed powder
a few basil leaves, chopped
juice of ½ lemon
1 tbsp peanut oil

Sauce

½ tbsp peanut oil
2 beef tomatoes, chopped
1 tsp garam masala
a pinch of turmeric
1 tsp chilli powder
½ bunch of fresh basil, chopped

Sprinkle the halibut with all the spices and lemon juice, and leave to marinate for 1 hour.

Meanwhile, make the sauce. Put the oil in a pan, and add the tomatoes, garam masala, turmeric and chilli powder. Simmer for an hour, then pass through a sieve. Add the basil.

Lightly pan-fry the marinated fish in the hot oil, about 2 minutes on each side, depending on the thickness of the pieces.

Serve the fish with the sauce, accompanied by a mound of rice.

Wine: A sweet German wine such as Auslese or a South Australian Riesling which is slightly dryer.

Antony Worrall Thompson
dell'Ugo

Antony Worrall Thompson is taking a very positive attitude to people's eating habits and actively encouraging the Mediterranean diet at his new restaurant dell'Ugo. He provides glamorous, inexpensive snacks which will encourage people to change their eating patterns because, unlike the nouvelle cuisine of the eighties, it doesn't leave you half starved.

Seafood Risotto with Scallop Tempura

SERVES 4

The shellfish

1 shallot, peeled and finely chopped
½ inch (1 cm) fresh ginger, peeled and finely chopped
1 garlic clove, peeled and finely chopped
1 tbsp extra virgin olive oil
5 fl oz (150 ml) dry white wine
1 lb (450 g) mussels, cleaned
16 clams, cleaned
5 pints (3 litres) fish stock

The squid

1 garlic clove, peeled and chopped
1 tbsp extra virgin olive oil
8 oz (225 g) squid, cleaned and cut into small pieces
2 plum tomatoes, skinned, seeded and diced
2 tbsp chopped fresh coriander
2 tbsp chopped flat parsley
2 tbsp finely chopped basil

The rice

1 onion, peeled and finely chopped
2 garlic cloves, peeled and finely chopped
½ hot chilli pepper, seeded and finely chopped
2 tbsp olive oil
1½ oz (25 g) unsalted butter
8 oz (225 g) arborio rice
1 pinch saffron, soaked in warm water
freshly grated Parmesan cheese to taste
salt and freshly ground black pepper

For the shellfish, sweat the shallot, ginger and garlic in

olive oil until soft but not brown. Add the white wine, bring to the boil and add mussels and clams. Cover and cook until the shellfish have opened, a few minutes only. Remove shellfish and set aside. Add the fish stock to the shellfish juices and bring to the boil. Simmer, covered, for 20 minutes and strain, keeping the broth for the risotto. Remove shellfish flesh from the open shells (discard any that have not opened) and chop.

For the squid, sweat the garlic in olive oil, then add the squid. Cook fast for 2 minutes, then add the tomatoes and herbs. Set aside.

For the risotto, sweat the onion, garlic and chilli in the olive oil and 1 tbsp of the butter until soft and bown. Add the rice, toss with the onions and cook for 1 minute. Add the simmering fish broth a little at a time, stirring frequently to avoid sticking. Wait until each addition is almost absorbed before adding the next. Add the saffron half-way through the cooking process. After about 18 minutes, when the rice is tender, add the squid mix, clams and mussels, Parmesan to taste and the remaining butter. Stir vigorously to combine.

To serve, top with scallop tempura (see overleaf), slice horizontally.

Scallop Tempura

8 large scallops
nori *seaweed*
8 oz (225 g) plain flour
10 fl oz (300 ml) beer
1½ oz (40 g) fresh yeast
a pinch of salt
vegetable oil for deep-frying

Remove the coral from the scallops (use in the risotto) and wrap the white flesh of each in *nori* seaweed.

Make the batter by placing the flour in a bowl and making a well in the centre. Add the beer, yeast and salt, and mix well to a smooth batter. Allow to rest in a warm place.

Heat oil in a suitable saucepan – or a wok – to around 180°C (360°F).

Meanwhile, using a fork, skewer or chopsticks, dip the *nori*-wrapped scallops into the batter, then gently immerse in the hot oil. Fry for 2 – 3 minutes until crisp and golden. Drain well on kitchen paper.

Seared Peppered Tuna Sashimi with Spicy Lentils

SERVES 4

*1 lb (450 g) loin of tuna (swordfish or monkfish),
  in the piece*
ground (not powdered) black pepper

Spicy lentils

8 oz (225 g) Puy lentils
3 garlic cloves, peeled
10 fl oz (300 ml) chicken stock
1 red onion, finely chopped
grated zest and juice of 4 limes
2 tbsp chopped fresh coriander
3 fl oz (85 ml) extra virgin olive oil
2 red chillies, seeded and finely diced
salt

To serve

1 baguette
olive oil
1 garlic clove, peeled
4 tbsp mayonnaise
1 tsp wasabi (Japanese horseradish)

Roll the tuna in ground black pepper. Heat a non-stick frying pan until it is white hot and sear the tuna for 30 seconds all over. Remove from the pan and allow to cool. Chill and then cut into ¼ inch (6 mm) slices.

For the lentils, place the lentils and garlic in a suitable pan, and cover with stock by about 1 inch (2.5 cm). Bring to the boil and cover. Simmer until cooked, adding more boiling stock if the lentils become too dry. The lentils should remain separate and should not be squashy.

Add all the other ingredients while the lentils are still warm. Season to taste with salt and pepper and cool.

Meanwhile, make the *crostini* and *wasabi* mayonnaise. Slice the baguette horizontally, drizzle with olive oil and place on a baking tray in a low oven – about 300°F (150°C) Gas 2 – until crisp and golden. Allow to cool, then rub with the clove of raw garlic. Mix the powdered *wasabi* with water following the instructions on the packet, and mix into the mayonnaise.

To serve, place a tablespoon of lentils in the centre of a plate. Arrange slices of tuna around one side of the lentils, garnish with the *crostini* and serve with the *wasabi* mayonnaise.

Steamed Mussels with Coriander, Greens and Lentil Broth

SERVES 4

4 tbsp olive oil
1 large onion, peeled and finely chopped
4 chilli peppers, seeded and finely chopped
4 garlic cloves, peeled and finely chopped
1 inch (2.5 cm) fresh ginger, peeled and finely chopped
4 tbsp plain flour
8 tbsp chopped fresh coriander
8 tbsp chopped parsley
10 fl oz (300 ml) dry white wine
10 fl oz (300 ml) fish stock
salt and ground black pepper
2 oz (50 g) butter
40 mussels, cleaned
a handful of cooked Puy lentils
3 oz (75 g) chopped greens, including spinach, radish
  tops, turnip tops

Heat the oil in a large casserole and sauté the onion, chilli, garlic and ginger. Add the flour and cook for 1 minute. Stir in the coriander, parsley, wine and fish stock, and season with salt and pepper to taste. Cover and simmer for 3 minutes. Add the mussels and cook for a further 5 minutes until the mussels open (discard any that remain closed).

Put the mussels on four plates. Fold the butter, lentils and greens into the broth, heat through, and pour into separate bowls. Serve both while hot.

Tomato and Bread Soup

SERVES 4

1 chilli pepper, seeded and finely chopped
2 onions, peeled and finely chopped
4 garlic cloves, peeled and crushed to fine paste with salt
4 tbsp good olive oil
1 sprig thyme
1 bay leaf
2 lb (900 g) ripe plum tomatoes, peeled and roughly
  chopped (with seeds)
1 tbsp tomato purée
1 small country loaf (preferably sourdough), soaked in
  10 fl oz (300 ml) chicken or vegetable stock
salt and ground black pepper
grated Parmesan cheese
basil leaves

Sweat the chilli, onions and garlic in olive oil with the thyme and bay leaf until cooked but not brown. Add the tomatoes and tomato purée and cook until very soft and broken down (about 20 minutes). Add the bread and stock. Season, cover, and simmer for 30 minutes. The soup should be very thick.

When ready to serve, add Parmesan and basil to taste. This soup can be served at room temperature.

Grilled Marinated Vegetable Salad

SERVES 4

Vegetables

1 yellow pepper, quartered and seeded
1 red pepper, quartered and seeded
1 aubergine, sliced lengthways
2 courgettes, sliced lengthways
2 small red onions, peeled, blanched whole for 5 minutes,
    and halved
1 fennel bulb, blanched whole for 2 minutes, and
    quartered
8 asparagus tips
olive oil

Grilled Vegetable Marinade

3 shallots, peeled and diced
3 red chilli peppers, seeded and finely diced
3 garlic cloves, peeled and diced
1 bunch basil leaves, cut into julienne strips
1/2 bunch oregano leaves, ripped
1 pint (600 ml) olive oil
3 tbsp sherry vinegar
salt and ground black pepper

Caponata

1 aubergine, peeled, sliced lengthways then cut in half
2 fl oz (50 ml) extra virgin olive oil
1/2 large onion, peeled and finely chopped
1 celery stick, diced
2 ripe tomatoes, skinned, seeded and chopped
2 oz (50 g) black olives, stoned
1 tbsp small capers
1 red pepper, roasted, skinned and diced

1 fl oz (25 ml) red wine vinegar
basil leaves to taste

Brush the prepared vegetables with olive oil and grill
either on a cast-iron oven-top grill or a barbecue. Allow to
cool.

Combine all the ingredients for the marinade. Place the
grilled vegetables in the marinade and leave overnight if
possible.

For the caponata, salt the aubergine and leave for 30
minutes; rinse in cold water and pat dry. In a frying pan,
cook the aubergines in about half of the olive oil for 5
minutes. Add the onion, celery, tomatoes, olives and
capers; cover and cook for 10 minutes. Remove from the
heat and add the rest of the ingredients including the
remaining oil; allow to cool.

To serve, spoon the caponata into the centre of a
serving plate. Arrange the marinated vegetables around
the caponata and garnish with two *crostini* (see page 246)
per person.

STEPHEN TERRY
The Canteen, Marco Pierre White

Under the tutelage of chefs such as Raymond Blanc, Albert Roux, Pierre Koffmann, Nico Ladenis and Marco Pierre White, a host of bright young stars is changing the face of British cuisine. Stephen Terry emerged from the steamy kitchens of chef Marco Pierre White at Harvey's to set up The Canteen, Marco Pierre White in London's Chelsea Harbour.

'We're aware that people can buy really good produce from Sainsbury's these days, and are tending to cook more for themselves. I think people are beginning to use their imaginations about salads for instance, and it's our job to fire that imagination. Think about the days when a salad meant a couple of lettuce leaves, a bit of cucumber and a tomato, and compare it with what we've got on the tables these days – at Harvey's we used to do a salad of warm potatoes cooked in chicken stock which we would drain and then douse with an olive oil vinaigrette. We'd add a few sardines and serve it on a bed of mixed leaves with plum tomatoes – you don't get much easier than that.'

Warm Salad of Rabbit
with Asparagus

SERVES 4

1 English lettuce heart
1 curly endive heart
1 oak leaf lettuce heart
8 sprigs of lambs lettuce
16 rocket leaves
12 radicchio leaves
2 lb (900 g) medium to fine asparagus stalks
2 large Jerusalem artichokes
10 fl oz (300 ml) olive oil
salt and pepper
2 large saddles of rabbit
4 sprigs of chervil
2 tbsp snipped chives
1 small black truffle (optional)

Vinaigrette

4 fl oz (120 ml) olive oil
1½ fl oz (40 ml) white wine vinegar

Preheat the oven to 425°F (220°C) Gas 7.

Wash and dry all the salad leaves, and keep covered with a damp towel and clingfilm in the refrigerator.

Wash and peel the asparagus and cook in boiling salted water for about 4 minutes until just cooked. Drain, refresh in ice cold water, and keep refrigerated.

Wash the Jerusalem artichokes well and thinly slice them to produce small circles. Heat the olive oil in a pan to deep-fry the artichoke slices. The oil must be hot enough for the 'crisps' to fry as soon as they go into the oil. Fry until crisp and golden-brown. Drain on kitchen paper, and season with a little salt.

Cut the belly flaps from the rabbit saddles. Heat a little

of the olive oil in a pan until very hot, then put in the seasoned belly flats and seal them. Repeat the same process with the rabbit saddles until sealed and starting to brown all over. Place in the hot oven and cook for about 8 minutes, turning half-way through. Remove the belly flaps after 2–3 minutes and slice them into thin strips, then fry them in them in more of the olive oil until they curl up and become crisp. Drain well. When cooked, allow the rabbit saddles to rest for 3–4 minutes, then remove the fillets from the bone.

Mix the vinaigrette ingredients together, seasoning to taste.

In a round bowl, season and dress the salad leaves with some of the vinaigrette, then divide them between the centres of four plates. Cut each asparagus stalk into four equal lengths, season again and dress with vinaigrette. Place in and around the salads. Next, slice the warm rabbit fillets into six equal pieces on an angle and place into the salad – again seasoning them individually and dressing them with a little vinaigrette first. Sprinkle some fried belly of rabbit over the salad with a few artichoke crisps. Garnish with the chervil, chives and some thin slices of black truffle (if used).

Wine: A typically South Australian spicy white – Suiraz Cabernet.

Red Mullet with Sauce Antiboise

SERVES 4

4 × 8 oz (225 g) red mullet, scaled and filleted
salt and pepper
plain flour
3 fl oz (85 ml) olive oil
14 oz (400 g) young spinach leaves, washed

Sauce

5 fl oz (150 ml) olive oil
3 shallots, peeled and finely chopped
1 garlic clove, peeled and crushed
10 plum tomatoes, skinned, seeded and diced
20 stoned black olives, quartered
10 large fresh basil leaves, sliced finely
10 large fresh coriander leaves, sliced finely
20 large fresh flat parsley leaves, sliced finely
lemon juice

To cook the red mullet, season the fish on both sides with salt and pepper and lightly flour.

Heat a little of the olive oil in a frying pan, and add the fillets, skin side down first. After about 2 minutes, when the fillets are starting to go golden-crisp, turn them over and finish cooking the other side, another 2 minutes or so. Keep warm.

Sauté the spinach in a little more olive oil in a pan for about 2–3 minutes so that the leaves retain their colour and freshness. Season, and keep warm.

To make the sauce, gently heat the olive oil in a small pan, add the shallot and garlic and allow to cook gently for 2–3 minutes without colouring. Add the tomato dice and then the olives, followed by the fresh herbs. Gently combine all the ingredients, remove from the heat and season with salt and pepper and lemon juice. Note that the sauce should not be allowed to become too hot or the tomatoes will turn to purée and the herbs will lose their freshness. The sauce should be served immediately.

To serve, place the spinach in the middle of the plate with the two red mullet fillets on top. Serve the sauce around, ensuring each plate has an equal amount of garnish.

Wine: A Mediterranean white, full and robust, such as Spanish Penedés or a Southern Italian.

Roast Rump of Lamb with Provençal Vegetables

SERVES 4

2 tbsp olive oil
4 medium rumps of lamb, boned (keep the bones)
salt and pepper
8 baby aubergines
3 medium courgettes
8 even new potatoes, cooked whole in their skins
5 plum tomatoes, skinned, quartered and seeded,
 to leave petals
3 red and 3 yellow peppers, roasted whole in olive oil
 and skinned (see page 178)
1 garlic clove, peeled and lightly crushed

Sauce

lamb bones from the rumps, chopped
1 small carrot, diced
½ small onion, peeled and diced
½ celery stick, diced
4 garlic cloves, peeled and halved
1 tbsp olive oil
2 tbsp brandy
3½ fl oz (100 ml) dry white wine
15 fl oz (450 ml) each of veal stock, chicken stock
 and water
1 chicken leg, boned and chopped
1 sprig each of fresh thyme and tarragon
5 white peppercorns
3 tomatoes, seeded and diced

Preheat the oven to 475°F (240°C) Gas 9.

To start the sauce, roast the lamb bones until golden-brown, about 15 minutes. Turn the oven off.

In a large pan over a medium heat, sweat the diced

vegetables and garlic in the olive oil. Cook for 4–5 minutes until just starting to brown a caramelise. Add the bones and deglaze with brandy. Add the white wine and reduce by half. Add all the stock and water and the chopped raw chicken. Bring to the boil, skim off any fat and add the herbs, spices and tomatoes and cook for 45 minutes. Pass through a fine sieve several times, then boil to reduce by half to the required consistency.

To cook the lamb and vegetables, preheat the oven again to 425°F (220°C) Gas 7. Heat half the olive oil in a large flat pan. When smoking hot, place the four seasoned rumps of lamb in the pan and cook until sealed and golden-brown on all sides. Put into the hot oven until cooked, about 10–11 minutes, turning over half-way through the cooking time. Remove from the oven and allow the lamb rumps to relax.

Slice the aubergines, courgettes and potatoes into ¼ inch (5 mm) slices. Cut the tomato petals in half and cut the pepper flesh into similar shapes. Season all the vegetables, and fry the aubergine, courgette and potato slices in the remaining olive oil with the garlic to infuse a subtle garlic flavour. When nearly cooked and golden, add the tomato and peppers. Cook for a further 2–3 minutes, then drain.

Slice each rump of lamb into eight or nine pieces, and arrange in the centre of the plate. Place the vegetables around the lamb. Bring the sauce to the boil. Season to taste, then pour on to the plates.

Wine: A subtle red such as Burgundy or New World Pinot
Noir or a light Spanish red such as Navarra.

Ravioli of Fresh Tuna and Coriander

SERVES 4

Ravioli

10¼ oz (290g) strong plain flour
3 egg yolks
2 whole eggs
1 tsp olive oil

Filling

14 oz (400 g) fresh tuna fish
1 tbsp freshly ground coriander
2 tbsp freshly ground black pepper
up to 1 pint (600 ml) olive oil
salt and pepper
2 tsp lemon juice
½ tbsp chopped fresh coriander leaves

Dressing

2 fl oz (50 ml) soy sauce
1 fl oz (25 ml) balsamic vinegar
1 tbsp olive oil
3½ fl oz (100 ml) peanut oil
salt, pepper and lemon juice to taste

Garnish

1 large English lettuce, washed and dried
½ tbsp olive oil
about 16 rocket leaves
4 petals of sun-dried tomatoes

For the ravioli pasta, combine all the ingredients in a food mixer. Remove, and mould into a ball. Cover in clingfilm and allow to rest in the fridge.

To make the filling, coat the tuna with the ground coriander and pepper. Place in one layer in a pan and cover with olive oil. Slowly cook for about 15 minutes. When cooked, allow to cool in the oil.

Remove the tuna from the oil and flake. Season with salt and pepper, lemon juice and chopped coriander leaves. Add a little of the cooking oil to hold the mixture together. Keep cool.

To make the ravioli, roll out one piece of the pasta dough gently on a floured surface and then feed it through a pasta machine several times until it is as thin as newspaper. Do the same with the rest of the dough, keeping it well covered when ready.

Using a pastry cutter, cut out 24 × 3¼ inch (8 cm) circles. Spoon a good helping of the filling into the centre of each of twelve of the circles. Leave a good clear edge all around the filling so that the circles of pasta can be sealed together well. Top with the other twelve circles and gently press the edges together. Using a 2¼ inch (6 cm) fluted cutter, cut the ravioli out and then pinch the edges all round again to ensure the seal is sound.

Drop the ravioli into boiling salted water for 30 seconds and then refresh immediately in cold water. Drain, place on a plate covered with a little olive oil and then cover with clingfilm and refrigerate. (The oil is to stop them sticking together.)

When you want to serve, mix the dressing ingredients together. Place the ravioli into boiling salted water for 3 minutes. Drain well.

For the garnish, heat a large frying pan with the olive oil, and sauté the lettuce leaves for 30 seconds. Season lightly. Place them evenly in the centre of four bowls. Thinly slice the sun-dried tomatoes and place on the lettuce.

Season the ravioli lightly and place three in each bowl on top of the lettuce leaves. Slightly warm the dressing and serve over and around the ravioli.

Wine: A Provence rosé or a provincial French country wine – Fitou.

Turbot with Braised Cabbage, Lentils and Girolles

SERVES 4
4 × 6 oz (175 g) turbot fillets
salt and pepper
olive oil
chicken stock

Lentils

8 oz (225 g) lentilles du Puy (green lentils), soaked in cold water for 12 hours
1 sprig of thyme
½ bay leaf
1 garlic clove, peeled

Cabbage

1 small Savoy cabbage
8 fresh sage leaves, sliced finely

Girolles

1 garlic clove, peeled and halved
1 shallot, peeled and finely chopped
8 oz (225 g) girolle mushrooms, cleaned
1 tsp each of finely diced carrot, celery and shallot

To cook the lentils, put them with thyme, bay leaf and garlic into a pan and cover with 17 fl oz (500 ml) chicken stock. Season with a little salt. Bring to the boil and cook gently for about 8–10 minutes. Strain, retaining the stock, and leave to one side.

To braise the cabbage, cut it into four, and separate the layers. Remove the large stalk from any pieces with a knife. Cut into fairly large strips.

Gently heat 4 tbsp of olive oil in a thick-bottomed pan.

Add the cabbage and sweat without colouring for 2–3 minutes. Add 10 fl oz (300 ml) of chicken stock, the fresh sage and a little seasoning. Cover with greaseproof paper and cook until tender, about 10–12 minutes. Keep warm.

To cook the girolles, rub the bottom of a frying pan with the cut garlic and place over a moderate heat. Add 2 tbsp of olive oil and gently sweat the chopped shallot until translucent. Add the girolles, and cook over a high heat until they release their liquid. Drain and cook for about 2 minutes more. Keep warm.

Sweat the vegetable dice for the lentils in 1 tbsp olive oil until soft. Add to the lentils and warm them through.

Season the turbot with salt and pepper and cook in a hot frying pan with 4 tbsp olive oil. Turn the turbot over when golden-brown on the first side (about 2½–3 minutes), then sauté for a further 2 minutes.

To serve, place the drained braised cabbage in the centre of each plate. Scatter lentils and girolles around the cabbage. Serve the turbot on the cabbage. Serve some of the cabbage cooking liquid over the lentil and girolles, as sauce.

Wine: Either a dry white from the Loire – Gros Plant or a white Bordeaux.

PHILIP HOWARD
The Square

Terry's stablemate, Philip Howard, is now the chef at The Square off Pall Mall. His cooking has a distinctive Provençal feel.

Fillet of Lamb with Grilled Aubergine and Herb-topped Tomato

This dish can also be made with noisettes of lamb, sautéed on the hob for 4 minutes per side

SERVES 4

2½ lb (1 kg) rump or fillet of lamb
2½ fl oz (75 ml) olive oil
1 aubergine, cut lengthways
2 tomatoes, halved
2 garlic cloves, peeled and cut
1 large bunch of parsley, chopped
½ tbsp chopped thyme
salt and pepper

Sauce

1 shallot, peeled and finely diced
1 garlic clove, peeled and crushed
2 tbsp olive oil
4 fl oz (120 ml) lamb stock
8 oz (225 g) tomatoes, finely diced

To Serve

quarters of roasted potatoes with skins on
freshly chopped flat parsley

Preheat the oven to 425°F (220°C) Gas 7.

Rub the lamb with a little of the oil, and roast for 10 minutes. Reduce the heat to 325°F (160°C) Gas 3, and cook for a further 10 minutes for rare, 20 minutes for medium. Remove from the oven, cover and allow to rest.

Meanwhile, preheat the grill. Brush the slices of aubergine with half the oil and grill for 6–8 minutes, turning once until cooked.

Rub each cut side of tomato with garlic. Heat the remaining oil and gently sweat the crushed garlic. Bring a large pan of water to a rapid boil and blanch the parsley for 1 minute. Drain immediately and stir into the garlic butter. Stir in the chopped thyme, salt and pepper. Spread this parsley butter over each half of tomato and heat through in the oven for 6 minutes.

For the sauce, sauté the shallot and garlic in the olive oil until softened. Discard fat from the meat juices and add these to the shallot pan with lamb stock. Bring to the boil. Season to taste and add the diced tomatoes and a little more olive oil.

To serve, slice the lamb and serve with the grilled aubergine, herbed tomato and the sauce accompanied by roasted potato quarters and sprinkled with chopped parsley.

Wine: A red Burgundy such as Rully which is light, soft and fruity or an earthy Chassagne.

Seared Scallops on a Dice of Provençal Vegetables

Scallops only need to be kissed by the heat. Here they are dressed with a sauté of diced provençal vegetables and served in the curved shell.

SERVES 4

4 large or 8 small scallops, opened, trimmed and corals removed
4 fl oz (120 ml) olive oil

Provençal vegetables

1 shallot, peeled and very finely chopped
1 garlic clove, peeled and crushed
1 sprig of thyme
1 small aubergine, very finely diced
2 courgettes, trimmed and very finely diced
1 red pepper, seeded, skinned and finely diced
salt and pepper
lemon juice to taste
2 tsp freshly chopped flat parsley or chives

To make the vegetables, heat a little of the oil, and gently sauté the shallot and garlic until softened. Add the sprig of thyme, diced vegetables and extra oil and sauté over a high heat until softened but not browned and still retaining some 'bite'.

Rub a large heavy-based skillet with olive oil and heat until extremely hot. If using large scallops, cut the white muscle into two rounds; leave small ones whole. Sear the nuggets of scallop on each side for 30 seconds to 1 minute depending on the heat of the pan. Remove immediately if they should begin to brown.

Season the sautéed vegetables and add lemon juice to lift the oil. Remove the thyme sprig and stir in the parsley or chives.

Place the seared scallops on a bed of sautéed vegetables in cup-shaped scallop shells.

Wine: A rich white such as a New Zealand or Australian Chardonnay.

Pissaladière with a Sauté of Wild Mushrooms

SERVES 4

1 tsp dried yeast
1½ fl oz (40 ml) warm water
a pinch of sugar
1 egg, beaten
4½ oz (125 g) plain flour
½ tsp salt
a drop of olive oil
a handful of rocket leaves, to garnish

Topping

1 lb (450 g) onions, peeled and sliced thinly
2 tbsp olive oil
2 sprigs of thyme
2 garlic cloves, peeled and crushed
black pepper

Wild mushroom sauté

14 oz (400 g) wild mushrooms
2 tbsp olive oil
1 shallot, peeled and finely diced
4 tomatoes, skinned, seeded and diced
1 tbsp chopped fresh parsley
1 tsp chopped fresh thyme

Preheat the oven to 375°F (190°C) Gas 5.

To make the pissaladière base, put the yeast in the water with the sugar and *half* the beaten egg, leave to become frothy, then mix in the other ingredients. Knead and leave the dough to rest for 30 minutes.

Roll out the dough until fine, place on a baking sheet, and prick.

For the topping, sweat the onions with oil, 1 sprig of thyme and the garlic until golden and soft. Smear this over the top of the uncooked base, and sprinkle with the remaining chopped thyme leaves and pepper. Bake for 15–20 minutes until crusty.

For the mushroom sauté, throw the mushrooms in hot olive oil, then add the shallot and sauté until soft. Add the diced tomato, parsley and thyme.

To serve, place the mushroom sauté on a bed of rocket leaves alongside a wedge of the onion tart.

Wine: An Italian – Orvieto.

JEAN-CHRISTOPHE NOVELLI
The Provence

Jean-Christophe Novelli of The Provence restaurant at
The Gordelton Mill Hotel in the New Forest, makes food
which looks like a work of art. Here are two recipes which
are easy enough to try at home.

Barigouole de Tourteaux
Crab with Artichokes

SERVES 4

4 cooked globe artichokes, stems attached
salt and pepper
1 tbsp each of lemon and lime juice
11 oz (300 g) white crab meat, plus the crab claws
2 tbsp chopped mixed fresh herbs (chervil, chives, parsley,
   dill)
2 tomatoes, skinned, seeded and diced
1–2 anchovy fillets, mashed
2 tbsp low-fat mayonnaise
1 cucumber, sliced thinly
extra virgin olive oil
a handful of lettuce leaves
8 oz (225 g) smoked salmon, cut into 4 thin slices
4 quail's eggs, cooked and shelled
a sprinkle of paprika
a few whole chives

Vinaigrette

8 fl oz (250 ml) olive oil
3½ fl oz (100 ml) Xérès (sherry) vinegar
1 tbsp chopped herbs

Prepare the cooked artichokes by removing the stems
leaves and the hairy insides or chokes. Keep the stems
Turn the hearts into a neat round shape if necessary
Season with salt, pepper, lemon and lime juice. Put aside

In a bowl, combine the white crab meat, herbs an
diced tomato. Mix the anchovy into the mayonnaise, an
add to the crab. Season to taste and refrigerate until read
to prepare the finished dish.

Make the vinaigrette by mixing the oil, vinegar an
herbs with some seasoning to taste.

Put a little oil on the cucumber slices, then arrange them in a circle on a large plate. Place the lettuce, seasoned with vinaigrette to taste, inside the cucumber circle. Arrange the artichoke hearts on the leaves.

Place spoonfuls of the crab mixture in the centre of the salmon slices. Roll up, and place, inverted, into the artichoke hearts. Sprinkle the salmon with olive oil, then place the stem of the artichoke on top of the salmon. Dip the small end of each quail's egg into paprika and place on top of the artichoke stem. Garnish with whole chives and the meat from the points of the crab claws.

Wine: Pouilly Fumé 1989.

Palette de Saumon, Tomate Confite aux Aromates 'Andaloux'

Thinly Sliced Salmon with Slowly Cooked Tomatoes in Olive Oil

SERVES 4

4 small beef tomatoes, skinned
salt and pepper
2 tbsp chopped mixed fresh herbs (thyme, dill, parsley, chives)
6 fl oz (175 ml) extra virgin olive oil
½ head of celery, trimmed
1 small aubergine, trimmed
1 each of orange, red, yellow, green and purple peppers, seeded
1 fennel bulb, trimmed
8 oz (225 g) button mushrooms, sliced
8 oz (225 g) wild mushrooms, sliced
½ oz (15 g) fresh ginger root, peeled and chopped finely
1 lb (450 g) salmon fillet, cut into 4 small pieces

Sauce

1 lb (450 g) tomatoes, skinned and seeded
a pinch of sugar
3 fl oz (85 ml) extra virgin olive oil

Make the sauce first. Place the tomatoes in a blender, and add salt, sugar and pepper to taste. Slowly add the olive oil, then pass through a fine sieve. Leave in a pan, ready to heat quickly when serving.

Cut the beef tomatoes into two halves and remove the seeds. Season and place some of the herbs on top. Sprinkle generously with some of the olive oil and leave for a few hours.

Cut up all the vegetables, some into small neat pieces, some into squares and some into diamonds. Place some of the olive oil in a large pan and slowly fry the vegetables plus the ginger for a few minutes until cooked to taste.

Season the salmon pieces and fry in olive oil, minutes only. Heat the tomato sauce through gently.

To dress the plates, place the top half of each tomato on the plate, upside-down, and fill with mixed vegetables. Place a piece of salmon on top and pour over the hot tomato sauce. Garnish with the remaining herbs and with the other half of the tomato.

Serve with rice.

Wine: A sauvignon – New Zealand Cloudy Bay 1990.

SIMON GUELLER
Millers

Simon Gueller is totally uncompromising about his menu at Millers in Harrogate. His Provençal cooking is what he *wants* to cook, and his customers 'can either like it or eat elsewhere' as far as he is concerned. Luckily, despite the occasional added cream, it's among the healthiest food the Mediterranean has to offer, and a three-course meal won't leave you feeling unable to stagger home. Here are some of the dishes he gave us.

Steamed Turbot
with Olive Oil, Shallots
and Balsamic Vinegar

SERVES 4 AS A STARTER

4 fl oz (120 ml) olive oil
3 oz (75 g) shallots, peeled and sliced
1 lb (450 g) fillet of turbot cut into 4
salt and pepper
4 tbsp balsamic vinegar

Heat the olive oil in a pan and gently cook the shallots until they start to colour. Steam the turbot for 5 minutes and season well with salt and pepper. Put the shallots and oil on the plates, then add the fish and sprinkle with balsamic vinegar.

Wine: A clean white such as Sancerre, Muscat or Chardonnay from the Loire, Alsace or Tuscany.

Asparagus Braised with Morels

SERVES 4

12 dried morels
1 pint (600 ml) chicken stock
2 lb (900 g) thin asparagus stalks, trimmed
*   and chopped*
1 sprig of thyme
juice of ½ lemon
salt and pepper

Soak the morels for 20 minutes in cold water. Bring the chicken stock to the boil and add the pieces of asparagus and the drained morels. Boil for 2 minutes, then add the thyme and lemon juice. Boil for 2 minutes more then season and serve in soup bowls.

Roast Salmon with Sun-dried Tomatoes

SERVES 4

4 oz (100 g) sun-dried tomatoes in olive oil
4 salmon portions, skinned and boned
juice of 1 lemon
salt and pepper

Preheat the oven to 400°F (200°C) Gas 6.

Drain the tomatoes over a roasting tray. Put the salmon pieces in the tray and coat completely with the oil. Chop the tomatoes and put on top of the salmon. Squeeze lemon juice over the salmon and season with salt and pepper. Cover with foil and roast in the hot oven for 20 minutes.

Wine: A biscuity, buttery wine such as a Chardonnay, either from California, Pouilly-Fuissé or from Western Australia.

Goose Breast with Peach and Armagnac

SERVES 4

2 goose breasts, weighing 1 lb (450 g) each
2 ripe peaches, stoned and chopped
2 shallots, peeled and chopped
1 oz (25 g) sugar
1 fl oz (25 ml) wine vinegar
1 tbsp Cointreau
2 tbsp Armagnac
5 fl oz (150 ml) chicken stock
salt and pepper

Preheat the oven to 400°F (200°C) Gas 6.

Trim the excess fat from the goose and criss-cross the skin with the point of a knife. Heat a roasting pan and brown the goose on both sides over heat. Put the pan into a hot oven with the goose fat-side down and roast for 8 minutes. Remove from the oven and wrap the goose in foil.

Add the chopped peach, shallots, sugar and vinegar in that order to another pan. Brown for 5 minutes then add the alcohols and chicken stock. Simmer for 2 minutes. Force through a sieve, season and whisk over heat. Pour over the goose breast which has been cut into slices and seasoned.

Wine: A white Châteauneuf du Pape, a South African Pinotage, Stellenbosch or a Spanish red – Valdepeñas.

Gratin of Oranges

SERVES 4

6 large seedless oranges

Sabayon

4 egg yolks
1 oz (25 g) sugar
7 fl oz (200 ml) sweet orange dessert wine

Peel and segment the oranges with a sharp knife. Divide between four heatproof plates.

For the sabayon, cream the yolks and sugar together, then whisk in the wine. Place over a bain-marie and cook, whisking continuously, until the sauce thickens.

Pour the sabayon over the oranges and place the plates under a red-hot grill until the dishes brown.

Serve with orange sorbet (optional).

Wine: Orange Muscat (Brown Bros – Australia).

Timbale of Fresh Fruit in Sauternes

SERVES 4

10 fl oz (300 ml) Sauternes
1 oz (25 g) powdered gelatine
4 oz (100 g) raspberries
4 oz (100 g) strawberries
4 oz (100 g) mango flesh
4 oz (100 g) firm banana flesh

Sauce

6 oz (175 g) raspberries
2 oz (50 g) sugar

Boil the Sauternes, add gelatine, and whisk to dissolve. Leave to cool until nearly setting.

Prepare all the fruit by cutting into small pieces with a sharp knife. Mix with the partially set jelly. Put in tea cups, and chill to set in the fridge for 2 hours.

Make the sauce by puréeing together the raspberries and sugar.

Divide the sauce between four plates. Dip the teacups in hot water, and turn out on to the sauce.

Wine: More Sauternes, if necessary.

EUGENE McCOY
McCoy's Tontine

Down the road in Staddlebridge, Eugene McCoy's Mediterranean feasts are meeting stiff resistance – or so he
claims. Here are some of the dishes he says they're turning
down.

Parfait Saumon

SERVES 2

4 tbsp extra virgin olive oil
10 oz (300 g) salmon thinly sliced into three flat pieces
6 basil leaves, shredded
2 tsp chopped fresh chilli, seeded
salt and pepper

In a non-stick frying pan, heat some of the oil and quickly cook the salmon, minutes only. Add the basil and chilli, and warm through. Season, and finish with the remaining oil served cold around the fish.

Serve with a leafy salad without any dressing other than lemon juice.

Wine: A soave such as Vigrette Calvarino 1990 or Sancerre Rosé 1991 for a little more body.

Prawns with Capsicum, Chilli and Coriander

SERVES 2
12 large peeled prawns

Marinade

1 garlic clove, peeled and crushed
juice of 3 limes
1 fresh green chilli, chopped
½ red and ½ green pepper (capsicum), chopped
1 gherkin, chopped
2 sprigs of fresh coriander
salt and pepper
½ tsp fresh grated ginger
6 tbsp olive oil
6 capers, chopped
1 shallot, peeled and chopped

Mix the marinade ingredients together and pour over the prawns in a glass dish. Place in fridge overnight.

Serve with *bruschetta*, (see page 170) and beware of garlic breath for at least 3 days . . .

Wine: Sancerre Henri Natter or a New Zealand Sauvignon – Cloudy Bay 1991.

GARY RHODES
The Greenhouse

Gary Rhodes is the chef at The Greenhouse in London's Mayfair, and is appearing increasingly on our television screens.

The Greenhouse serves 'good old English food'. Its sticky puddings may not be the best bet for a healthy heart, but Rhodes insists that there's plenty on his menu which could feature in this book.

'The Mediterranean diet isn't restricted to food from Spain, France and Italy. There are plenty of traditional British dishes which have been around for centuries which are extremely good for you.'

Scallops with Artichokes and Asparagus

SERVES 4

8 asparagus stalks, trimmed
salt and pepper
2 large artichokes
juice of 1 lemon
1 shallot, peeled and chopped very finely
½ carrot, chopped very finely
1 celery stick, chopped very finely
extra virgin olive oil
3 tomatoes, chopped
1 garlic clove, peeled and chopped
1 tbsp mixed chopped fresh herbs (tarragon, basil and thyme)
5 fl oz (150 ml) white wine
a handful of mixed lettuce leaves (curly endive, lollo rosso, oak leaves, rocket)
12 scallops out of the shell and cleaned

Vinaigrette

6 tbsp olive oil
3 tbsp groundnut oil
3 shallots, peeled and chopped
2 garlic cloves, peeled and halved
1 tsp each of chopped fresh herbs (basil, thyme and tarragon)
8 black peppercorns
1 bay leaf
2 tbsp balsamic vinegar

Make the vinaigrette first. Simply allow all the ingredients to steep together until needed, then strain. This makes more than you need, but it can happily store in the fridge.

Peel the asparagus and blanch in boiling salted water

until tender, about 2 minutes. Refresh in cold water immediately.

Break off the outer leaves and the stalk of the artichoke. Cut a line 1½ inches (4 cm) from the base of each one until you have a disc. Coat all cut edges with lemon juice.

In a pan, sweat the shallot, carrot and celery in 2 fl oz (50 ml) of the olive oil until soft, then add the chopped tomato, garlic and herbs. Cook for a few minutes over a moderate heat. Add the wine and reduce by boiling until almost dry. Add 1½ pints (850 ml) water and allow to cook for a few minutes.

Place the prepared artichokes in the liquid you've just made. Allow the artichokes to simmer slowly until tender, about 15–20 minutes, then leave to cool. When cold, remove the centre of the artichoke and cut out the remaining hairs.

Cut the asparagus into 1 inch (2.5 cm) lengths, and the artichoke discs into five slices each. Pick over and wash the leaves. Dress the salad leaves with vinaigrette to taste. Warm the asparagus and the artichokes through in a little more olive oil and some of the dressing.

Sauté the scallops in a very hot pan, browning for 1 minute on both sides.

To serve, scatter asparagus and artichokes across the plate. Build the salad leaves into a mound in the centre, and place the scallops around. Drizzle more olive oil on top.

Wine: Intense, such as a Chardonnay.

Soused Mackerel on Warm Potatoes

SERVES 4

1 sprig each of basil, tarragon and thyme
1 star anise
1 leek, shredded
2 carrots, slices
1 celery stick, sliced
1 fennel bulb, sliced
6 shallots, peeled and sliced into rings
2 fl oz (50 ml) extra virgin olive oil
5 fl oz (150 ml) white wine
5 fl oz (150 ml) white wine vinegar
4 mackerel fillets, bones removed
2 tbsp chopped fresh parsley

Potatoes

8 oz (225 g) cooked mashed potatoes
salt and pepper
2 tbsp low-fat milk, or more as necessary
2 tbsp olive oil
2 shallots, peeled and chopped very finely
juice of ½ lemon

Make a bouquet garni by wrapping the herbs and star anise in a little muslin bag, or use the outer leaves of the leek to make a parcel which you can tie with string.

Sweat all the vegetables in oil with the bouquet garni for a few minutes. Add the white wine, vinegar and 1 pint (600 ml) water. Allow to cook until the vegetables are tender, about 10 minutes.

Slowly poach the mackerel fillets in enough of the water to cover, about 5 minutes.

Season the mashed potatoes with salt and pepper. Add a little milk, olive oil, chopped shallot and lemon juice, and whisk until the potatoes have a velvety texture; they should be very slightly runny on the plate.

To serve, put a tablespoon of potatoes on to each plate and place the drained mackerel on top. Finish with a little of the soused liquid and chopped parsley.

Wine: A light wine such as a Loire or Muscadet.

PAUL FLYNN
Nico at Ninety

Nico Ladenis at Chez Nico, Simply Nico and the recently
opened Nico at Ninety, is a big fan of Provençal food.
'Everything is sun-dried in Provence,' he said, dreaming
of his home in Draguignan. 'We're surrounded by fields of
peppers, courgettes, olive trees and there's a mill nearby
so we can have our own oil.' His chef at Nico at Ninety,
Paul Flynn, gave us some of his Provençal-influenced
dishes.

Prawn Cocktail

SERVES 2

12 large Scottish prawns, cooked
3½ fl oz (100 ml) mayonnaise
3 baby Little Gem lettuces, sliced finely
2 oz (50 g) potatoes, peeled and cut into
   ½ inch (1 cm) dice
2 oz (50 g) cucumber, cut into ½ inch (1 cm) dice
3 tbsp olive oil

Red pepper purée

2 oz (50 g) onions, peeled and sliced
4 red peppers, seeded and finely chopped
1 garlic clove, peeled
3½ fl oz (100 ml) olive oil
a dash of Worcestershire sauce
salt and cayenne pepper

For the red pepper purée, sweat the pepper, onion and
garlic in a little of the olive oil until soft. Place in a blender
and add the remainder of the olive oil, Worcestershire
sauce and salt and cayenne pepper to taste. This makes
more than you need for the recipe, but it will keep well in
the fridge for a few days. Use only 3½ fl oz (100 ml).

To assemble each dish, place six prawns on a plate
inside a pastry ring mould, and cover very neatly with
mayonnaise. Add a neat layer of red pepper purée on top
of the mayonnaise and then the finely sliced lettuce. Toss
the cucumber and potatoes in the olive oil, and season.
Place carefully around the pastry ring, then remove the
ring mould.

Mediterranean Red Mullet
with Rocket and Orange

SERVES 1

1 red mullet fillet
¾ oz (20 g) plain flour
1 bunch of rocket
2 tbsp olive oil
½ tbsp sherry vinegar
6 orange segments
juice of 2 oranges
2 tsp cornflour
salt and pepper
juice of 1 lemon

Lightly flour the red mullet fillet. Wash the rocket and dry it gently. Put 1 tbsp of the olive oil in a bowl and add the sherry vinegar.

For the sauce, dice the orange segments. Boil the orange juice. Thicken it with the cornflour until coating consistency and add the segments to the finished sauce. Do not boil the sauce once the segments have been added to it.

Heat the remaining olive oil in a frying pan. Place the red mullet, skin side down, in the pan and cook until brown, turning once. Remove the mullet from the pan when it is cooked, and lightly season with salt and pepper and lemon juice; drain on kitchen paper.

Place the red mullet on a plate. Toss the rocket leaves in the olive oil and sherry vinegar and place beside the fish, spooning the dressing over it.

Wine: Sancerre.

RAYMOND BLANC
Le Manoir aux Quat' Saisons

The king of curative cuisine must undoubtedly be Raymond Blanc at Le Manoir aux Quat' Saisons in Oxfordshire. Not only does he make a mean Mosaique de Gibiers aux Noisettes et Champignons Sauvages, but he's even planning on building a health spa at the restaurant next year. 'Eating well isn't just good for the senses,' he told us as we dodged the army of thirty-five chefs and waiters in Le Manoir's kitchen, 'but it's also a cure'. Le Manoir will be serving ginger and honey to its ailing customers in the next year or two while Raymond thumbs through the recipe books of the Chinese sages. Meanwhile, here are two of the treats he gave us for lunch.

Filets de Rouget Poêlés au Tian d'Aubergines et de Courgettes, Coulis de Tomates
Pan-fried Fillets of Red Mullet on an Aubergine, Tomato and Courgette Base, with a Tomato Coulis

SERVES 4

8 red mullet fillets
about 2 fl oz (50 ml) olive oil
salt and pepper

Tian of vegetables

2 tomatoes, sliced
1 courgette, sliced
½ aubergine, sliced

Dried fish seasoning

¾ oz (20 g) dried thyme
2 tsp dried rosemary
½ tsp each of dried orange and lemon zest

Tomato and olive oil coulis

6 ripe tomatoes, chopped
a tiny knob of butter
3½ fl oz (100 ml) olive oil
a pinch of sugar

Preheat the oven to 400°F (200°C) Gas 6.

Sprinkle the aubergine slices with salt and leave for 30 minutes to allow the bitter juices to be drawn out. Rinse in cold water.

For the tian of vegetables, brush the tomatoes with about 1 tsp of the olive oil, season with salt and pepper and bake in the oven for 5 minutes. Blanch the courgettes in lightly salted boiling water and then pan-fry in 1 tsp olive oil. Season with salt and pepper. Pan-fry the aubergine in about 1 tbsp olive oil for 3–4 minutes. Season with salt and pepper.

Lay the rings of tomato, aubergine and courgettes alternately on pieces of oiled paper to form four rectangles of about 4 × 3 inches (10 × 7.5 cm). Reserve.

Roughly chop the dried fish seasoning ingredients, and mix well.

For the tomato and olive coulis, purée the chopped tomatoes and pass through a fine sieve. Warm the tomato coulis (do *not* boil), and whisk in the butter followed by the olive oil. Season with salt and pepper and add sugar if necessary.

Pan-fry the red mullet in a little olive oil for 15 seconds on the flesh side, turn over and pan-fry on the skin side for 1 minute. Sprinkle with the dried fish seasoning. Place in the oven for 1 minute for medium rare.

To serve, place a tian of vegetables in the centre of each plate, using a fish slice, and place two fillets of red mullet in a cross on top. Pour the tomato and olive oil coulis around the tian.

Wine: A red Burgundy such as Bourgogne Passetout-grains or a white Mediterranean peasant wine from a jug, perhaps Domestica from Greece.

Côtelettes d'Agneau de Lait Rôties au Jus à la Tapenade

Roasted New Season Lamb Cutlets served with a Tapenade Juice

Vegetables such as ratatouille, braised fennel and French beans would accompany this dish perfectly.

SERVES 2

4 × 3 oz (75 g) lamb cutlets
2 tbsp olive oil
salt and pepper
a large pinch of mixed herbs (see below)

Mixed herbs

4 tsp dried thyme
2 tsp dried rosemary
1 tsp dried marjoram

Tapenade

2 tbsp extra virgin olive oil
1 garlic clove, peeled and puréed finely
2 anchovy fillets, washed to remove excess salt
a pinch of ground black pepper
4½ oz (125 g) stoned black olives (about 40 olives)

Juice

2 lb (900 g) lamb bones and trimmings,
   chopped finely
3½ fl oz (100 ml) olive oil
2 oz (50 g) fennel bulb, diced
4 oz (100 g) onions, peeled and diced

4 tomatoes, seeded and chopped
1 garlic clove, peeled and chopped
2 sprigs of thyme, chopped
1 sprig of rosemary, chopped
4 oz (100 g) courgettes, cut into ⅛ inch (3 mm) dice

The mixed herbs recipe will make more than you need in this recipe, but the combination is useful. Chop or grind the dried herbs, but not too finely, with a large pinch each of salt and pepper.

For the tapenade, blend all the ingredients together in a liquidizer until you obtain a very fine texture. Reserve.

Preheat the oven to 425°F (220°C) Gas 7.

To prepare the juice, heat the olive oil in a roasting tray, and sear the chopped bones and trimmings until dark in colour. Add the diced fennel and onion and roast in the hot oven for 30 minutes. Add the chopped tomato during the last 5 minutes. Remove the tray from the oven, skim off and remove the fat, then pour in some cold water. Scrape up the caramelized juices from the bottom of the tray. Pour into a large saucepan, cover the contents with cold water, and bring to the boil. Skim, then simmer for a further 30 minutes. Add the chopped garlic, thyme and rosemary during the last 5 minutes. Taste, correct seasoning with salt and pepper, and strain into a small casserole.

Blanch the courgette dice for 30 seconds in boiling salted water, refresh under cold water, and reserve.

To cook the cutlets, heat the olive oil in a sauté pan and colour the cutlets for 1 minute on each side. Season with salt and pepper and sprinkle with the mixed herbs. Roast for 6 minutes in the oven.

Meanwhile, warm the juice through, and whisk in 5 oz (150 g) of the tapenade and the courgette dice at the last moment.

Remove the fat from the lamb dish and let the lamb rest in a warm place for 2 minutes. Serve to your guests with the tapenade juice.

Wine: A Macedonian red from Greece or a Beaujolais –
Chiroubles or Fleurie.

Restaurants by Country

The Mediterranean Diet, based on mono-unsaturated fat, a high proportion of vegetables and very little dairy produce, is not by any means limited to the food of Southern Europe. In the Far East, milk, butter and cream are almost never used. We asked three chefs from South Asian restaurants to suggest recipes which follow the optimum nutritional guidelines.

THAI
The Blue Elephant

The Blue Elephant is one of London's oldest Thai restaurants, and serves its food, the ingredients of which are flown over from Bangkok the previous day, with the sort of elegance and charm known only in the Far East. It can be difficult to obtain some of the ingredients crucial to Thai cuisine but supermarkets are increasingly catching on to the fact that their customers are demanding more interesting foods. As a result, you may well be able to buy lemongrass and tamarind juice at your local supermarket. Ask for *tua fak yoo* (see Jungle Salad on page 306) however, and you might get a few raised eyebrows. (Try a Chinese or Thai supermarket.)

Vermicelli Salad

SERVES 1 AS A STARTER

7 oz (200 g) rice vermicelli
½ oz (15 g) dried prawns
4 oz (100 g) chicken breast, skinned
1 shallot, peeled and cut finely
3 red chillies, seeded and chopped
4 garlic stems, finely chopped (or chopped garlic clove
    and chives)
1 carrot, chopped finely
4 tsp fish sauce (nam pla)
5 tbsp lemon juice
1 tsp salt
1 tsp sugar
1 tbsp olive oil

Soak the vermicelli in warm water until soft, then cook in
hot water for 3 minutes. Drain well, and cut into 3 inch
(7.5 cm) pieces. Place in a bowl.

Reconstitute the dried prawns by heating briefly in hot
water. Cut into small pieces.

Cook the chicken in boiling water – about 15 minutes –
then drain well and cut into small pieces.

Add the chicken and prawn and the rest of the ingredients to the vermicelli in the bowl, and mix well.

Wine: A big white such as Crozes Hermitage from North-
        ern Rhône, an Italian Corvo or a South Australian
        Chardonnay.

Jungle
Salad

SERVES 2

2 oz (50 g) pak bung (swamp morning glory) cut into
  ¾ inch (2 cm) pieces (use spinach or any greens)
2 oz (50 g) tua fak yoo (yard-long bean) cut into ½ cm)
  pieces
2 oz (50 g) aubergine, cut into ½ inch (1 cm) cubes
1 oz (25 g) fresh baby corn, cut into ½ inch (1 cm) pieces
1 oz (25 g) carrot, cut into small cubes
1 oz (25 g) bean sprouts
2 oz (50 g) chicken breast, cooked and shredded
  (see previous recipe)

Sauce

4 fl oz (120 ml) coconut milk
1 oz (25 g) red curry paste
4 oz (100 g) tinned tuna fish
1½ tbsp tamarind juice
1½ tbsp sugar
1½ tbsp fish sauce (nam pla)
1 tbsp roasted sesame seeds

Boil all the vegetables separately until cooked, then drain
well.

   To make the sauce, boil the coconut milk on a low heat,
then add the red curry paste and stir until brown, about 10
minutes. Add the tuna fish and continue stirring until well
mixed. Add the rest of the ingredients.

Serve the vegetables on a plate with the shredded chicken on top. Pour the sauce over the chicken.

Choa Phaya

Kop, the head chef at The Blue Elephant, describes this dish as 'grilled rainbow trout wrapped in a banana leaf, served with two separate sauces, the green sauce as fiery as a volcano, the brown sauce as sweet as a first kiss'.

SERVES 1

1 × 11 oz (300 g) whole rainbow trout
1 tbsp Maggi sauce
1 tsp each of salt and pepper
1 banana leaf, softened in hot water

Volcano sauce

3 green chillies
1 garlic clove, peeled
1 tsp coriander root (or leaves), chopped
1½ tbsp fish sauce (nam pla)
2 tbsp lemon juice

First kiss sauce

10 tbsp tamarind juice (see below)
5 tbsp palm sugar (or brown sugar)
2 tbsp fish sauce (nam pla)
1 shallot, peeled and cut into fine strips

Make the sauces first.

For the Volcano Sauce, blend chillies, garlic and coriander root until well mixed and forming a paste. Add the fish sauce and lemon juice.

For the First Kiss Sauce, boil the tamarind juice. (If buying the tamarind fruit rather than the juice, soak it in warm water for about 10 minutes and squeeze the mixture for the juice.) Add the palm sugar and fish sauce to the tamarind, and simmer until the mixture turns to a light syrup. Fry the strips of shallots until brown, and sprinkle over the sauce.

Clean the fish and dry well. Par-grill both sides and place on a tray. Rub Maggi sauce, salt and pepper on both sides and then wrap in a banana leaf. Grill until cooked, another 10 minutes or so.

Wine: A New Zealand Sauvignon – Cloudy Bay, Pouilly Fumé from the Loire or Sauvignon/Sémillon from Chile.

Scallop Farang

SERVES 1

4 oz (100 g) scallops
1 tbsp peanut or sunflower oil
1 oz (25 g) broccoli, cut into 1 inch (2.5 cm) pieces
4 button mushrooms, sliced
4 fresh young baby corn, trimmed
½ oz (15 g) spring onion, cut into 1 inch (2.5 cm) pieces
½ oz (15 g) carrot, cut into long strips
½ oz (15 g) bean sprouts
1 tbsp oyster sauce
1 tsp Maggi sauce

Heat the oil on a high heat and add the scallops. Stir-fry
for about 2 minutes, then add the broccoli, mushroom and
corn. Continue to stir-fry for 2–3 minutes, then add the
rest of the ingredients and stir-fry until well cooked.

Wine: Try a dry or medium sherry – Fino or Montillado
or, perhaps, something which would provide an
interesting contrast such as a Sauternes or Californian Essencia Orange Muscat.

Chicken Salad

SERVES 1

7 oz (200 g) chicken meat, minced
2 tbsp lemon juice
2 tbsp fish sauce (nam pla)
½ tsp sugar
2 shallots, peeled and chopped finely
3 tbsp finely chopped spring onions
1 tbsp finely chopped lemongrass
1 tbsp finely chopped makrut (lime leaves)
2 tbsp chopped fresh mint
1 tbsp coconut milk
1 tbsp grated roasted rice

Nam prik pao sauce

3 shallots, peeled
1 garlic clove, peeled
10 dried red chillies, soaked in warm water until soft
a dash of peanut oil
a pinch each of salt and sugar

For the chilli sauce, fry the ingredients in a dash of olive oil until light brown, then blend well until they form a paste. Add sugar and salt to taste.

Prepare the dish by boiling the chicken – minutes only – and leaving to drain well. Put it in a dish, and firstly add the lemon juice, fish sauce, sugar and ½ tsp of the *nam prik pao*. Stir well. Add the rest of the ingredients and stir again.

Wine: An intense white – a Canadian Chardonnay such as Imiskillan or Chablis or a white Portuguese such as Bairrada.

Mixed Vegetables Blue Elephant

SERVES 4

½ tbsp peanut or sunflower oil
7 oz (200 g) broccoli, cut into 1 inch (2.5 cm) pieces
4 oz (100 g) mange-tout, trimmed
4 oz (100 g) Chinese cabbage, cut into 1 inch (2.5 cm)   pieces
2 oz (50 g) bean sprouts
1 tsp Maggi sauce
1 tbsp chicken stock
2 tbsp oyster sauce

Heat the oil on a high heat and add all the vegetables. Stir-fry until par-cooked, then add the Maggi sauce, chicken stock and oyster sauce. Continue to stir-fry until cooked, about 2–3 minutes more.

Ben's Thai Restaurant

The Blue Elephant's food may be food for fantasy, but Thai food need not be out of reach of the average cook. Ben's Thai restaurant in Maida Vale, London serves inexpensive straightforward food which is just as healthy.

The stir-fry recipes involve little more than mixing fresh ingredients. Use Italian vermicelli if you can't find rice vermicelli in your supermarket.

Kwaitiew Pad Thai

SERVES 1

4 oz (100 g) raw chicken or beef, cubed
1 tbsp peanut oil
2 eggs
6 oz (175 g) rice vermicelli, soaked (see page 305)
1 tbsp sugar
1½ tbsp fish sauce (nam pla)
½ oz (15 g) shelled peanuts
juice of 1 lemon
1 oz (25 g) bean sprouts
1 oz (25 g) carrots, peeled and chopped finely
2 spring onions, chopped

Fry the meat in half the oil, and scramble the eggs. Keep warm.

Drain the rice vermicelli well, then stir-fry in the remaining oil in a wok with the sugar, fish sauce, nuts and lemon juice. Add the bean sprouts, chopped carrots and spring onion, heat through, and throw over the meat and eggs.

Wine: Light reds such as Dão from Portugal, a light claret or a Bulgarian Cabernet Sauvignon.

Pad Priew Wan

SERVES 1

4 oz (100 g) raw mixed meats, cubed
1 tbsp peanut oil
½ onion, peeled and chopped finely
1 oz (25 g) carrots, peeled and chopped finely
2 tomatoes, chopped
1 oz (25 g) pineapple flesh, chopped
2 tbsp tomato sauce
2 tbsp fish sauce (nam pla)
1 tbsp sugar
2 spring onions, chopped

Stir-fry the meat in the oil in a wok, then add the onion, carrots, tomato and fruit. Add the sauces and sugar, mix in, then sprinkle with chopped spring onions before serving.

Wine: A spicy white Alsace Gewürztraminer or a Beaujolais such as Juliénas or a red Barbera D'Alba from Piedmont.

Tord Kra Tiem

SERVES 1

4 oz (100 g) raw mixed meats, cubed
1 tbsp peanut oil
½ onion, peeled and chopped
½ tbsp garlic powder
1 tbsp sugar
1 tbsp oyster sauce
½ tbsp freshly ground black pepper
1 tbsp fish sauce (nam pla)
1 tbsp fresh chopped coriander

Stir-fry all the ingredients together in a wok, a few
minutes only.

Khao Pad

SERVES 2

4 oz (100 g) raw meat of your choice, cubed
2 tbsp peanut oil
1 egg, beaten
1 oz (25 g) carrots, peeled and cubed
1 oz (25 g) cabbage, shredded
1 oz (25 g) onion, peeled and chopped
1 garlic clove, peeled and crushed
8 oz (225 g) cooked rice
1 tbsp soy sauce
½ tbsp fish sauce (nam pla)
1 tsp sugar
2 spring onions, chopped

Stir-fry the meat in half the oil, then remove. Add the egg, and cook to an 'omelette'. Remove and chop.

Add the remaining oil to the work or pan and stir-fry the vegetables, followed by the rice. After 2 minutes over a high heat, add the sauces and sugar. Heat through with the meat and egg strips. Garnish with the spring onions.

Wine: A Chinese Chardonnay Tsing Tao – a very fruity wine or a Romanian Pinot Noir.

CHINESE
Zen NW3

Zen NW3 is one of the five monosodium glutamate
(MSG)-free Chinese restaurants in the Zen group in
London. They've been practising a policy of healthy
eating for years, and gave us the recipes for some of our
favourite dishes.

Sea Bass with Tangerine Peel

You can buy tangerine peel from a Chinese supermarket, or try low-oven or sun-drying your own.

SERVES 4

1 tbsp dried tangerine peel
1 lb (450 g) whole sea bass

Sauce

1 tsp grated fresh root ginger
1 tbsp water
2 tbsp chicken stock
2 tbsp soy sauce
1 tsp Maggi sauce
1 tsp sugar
2 tbsp fresh chopped coriander

Put the sliced peel with pith removed on top of the cleaned fish, and a little inside, and steam for 12–14 minutes.

Boil the ginger in the water and stock to reduce a little, then add the soy, Maggi and sugar. Put the sauce on top of the fish, and cover with chopped spring onions and coriander.

Wine: A clean white such as Magdelene Rivaner from Pulham, Norfolk, a German Baden Dry or Sauvignon de St Brie from Burgundy.

Chicken Grilled with Coriander

SERVES 4

*4 chicken breasts, cut into large strips, skin and fat
    removed*
4 eggs, beaten
2 tbsp chopped fresh coriander
2 tbsp cornflour
2 tbsp ground coriander
salt and pepper

Dip

2 tbsp fish sauce
juice of ½ lemon
1 garlic clove, peeled and crushed
1 fresh green chilli, chopped
1 tsp sugar

Marinate the chicken strips in the eggs, coriander, cornflour, ground coriander and seasoning for 30 minutes, and then grill until tender.

Make a dip out of the fish sauce, lemon juice, garlic, chopped chillies and sugar.

Eat the chicken pieces with chopsticks, dipping them into the sauce.

Wine: Tavel Rosé from South Rhône, a white Burgundy –
    St Vétan or an Alsace red such as Pinot Noir.

ISRAELI
The Olive Tree

The cuisine provided by Freddie Kojuman at The Olive Tree is largely Israeli although Freddie comes from Iraq. He uses lots of chick-peas, lentils and rice because, as he says, meat is too expensive for many people in the Middle East and vegetarian meals are just as tasty.

Aubergine Yoghurt

SERVES 4

2 × 11 oz (300 g) aubergines
salt
wholemeal flour
olive oil for shallow-frying
2 garlic cloves, peeled and crushed
1 lb (450 g) plain yoghurt

Cut the aubergines in half, cube and salt to remove the bitter juices. Leave to drain for 3 hours, or if heavily seeded, 8 hours. (The Dutch aubergines are less bitter and need much less time to drain.) Rinse and dry well.

Toss the aubergine cubes in flour and fry in very hot oil. Remove, drain very well, and cover with a mixture of the crushed garlic and yoghurt.

Aubergine à la Greque

SERVES 4

2 × 11 oz (300 g) aubergines, salted and drained
  (see previous recipe)
½ tsp French mustard
1 pickled cucumber
a small bunch of parsley
1 red pimento, finely chopped
2 tbsp wine vinegar
salt and pepper
juice of 2 lemons
olive oil

Shallow fry the aubergines as in the previous recipe, drain well and place in a dish.

Mix all the other ingredients together with 2 tbsp olive oil, and pour over the aubergines. Leave for a while before serving.

Wine: A clean, sharp, fresh wine such as an Alsace Pinot Blanc, Umbrian Pinot Grigio or a dry Mosel.

Bamya
Okra

SERVES 4

1 large onion, peeled and chopped
1 small fresh green or red chilli, chopped
1 green pepper, seeded and chopped
2 tbsp olive oil
3 garlic cloves, peeled and chopped
salt and pepper
1 tbsp mixed herbs
2 medium tomatoes, chopped
1 tsp tomato purée
2 small tins of okra, drained, or 3 lb (1.4 kg) fresh okra,
   washed

Put the onion, chilli and pepper in a pan with the oil and
garlic. Add the salt, pepper and mixed herbs, and fry until
the onions brown. Add the chopped tomatoes and the
tomato purée. If the sauce is too thick, add a little water.
When simmering, throw in the okra with the lemon juice.
Leave for 3–4 minutes and serve.

Baba Ganush

SERVES 4

*2 × 11 oz (300 g) aubergines, salted and drained (see page
   323)*
2 tbsp tahina paste
juice of 2 lemons
2 garlic cloves, peeled and chopped
salt and pepper
2 tbsp olive oil
2 tbsp chopped fresh parsley

Pierce the aubergines all over and either char on top of the
gas flame, or grill. (The burnt taste adds to the flavour of
the dish.) When charred and blistered all over, put the
aubergines in cold water and remove the skins. Chop and
leave to one side.

   Blend the tahina, lemon juice, garlic and seasoning with
a little water and mix with the chopped aubergines.
Drizzle with the olive oil and garnish with parsley.

Hummus

Use either tinned or fresh chick-peas. If fresh, soak overnight, then boil for 2 hours in fresh water until soft. You'll get a better result if you boil them in a pressure cooker with a little salt and ½ tsp of bicarbonate of soda for 30 minutes.

SERVES 4

6 oz (175 g) dried chick-peas, cooked,
  or 12 oz (350 g) tinned, drained
5 fl oz (150 ml) water
5 oz (150 g) tahina paste
juice of 2 lemons
2 garlic cloves, peeled
2 tbsp olive oil

Place all the ingredients in a blender and purée to a smooth consistency.

Wine: Hummus could stand up to a red such as Côteaux du Tricastin from South Rhône, Montepulciana d'Abruzza from Italy or a fino sherry.

Chicken Kebab

SERVES 4

*1 × 4 lb (1.7 kg) chicken, boned, or 6 chicken
  breasts, cubed*

Marinade

1 tbsp olive oil
½ tsp salt
Freshly ground black pepper
2 cloves, lightly crushed
1 garlic clove, peeled and chopped
juice of 1 lemon
2 fl oz (50 ml) dry white wine
1 tsp Marsala

Mix the marinade ingredients together. Put the chicken
into the marinade, cover, and leave in the fridge overnight.

Skewer and grill, preferably over charcoal.

Wine: A red Gamory de Touraine from the Loire, a
       Spanish Rioja or a red Château Musar from the
       Lebanon.

Carrots in Sesame Oil

SERVES 4

2 lb (900 g) carrots, peeled and chopped
2 drops sesame oil
2 tsp olive oil
1 tsp mushroom soy sauce
a handful of sesame seeds

Stir-fry the chopped carrots in a wok with the sesame oil and olive oil. When soft or *al dente*, add the mushroom soy sauce, then remove. Scatter the sesame seeds over the carrots, and serve.

GREEK
Daphne's

Many people think that Greek food consists mainly of large chunks of meat, but Anna and Panikos Lymbouri who run Daphne's restaurant in Camden Town, include many vegetarian dishes on their menu. Lentils and pulses, which make up a major part of the diet in rural Greece, are used imaginatively along with traditional items such as tomatoes and olives.

Fasoles

SERVES 2

8 oz (225 g) dried white haricot beans
4 celery sticks, cut roughly into ½ inch (1 cm) strips
3 potatoes, peeled and cut into large cubes
salt and pepper
1 tbsp olive oil
juice of 1 lemon
1 tbsp finely chopped parsley

Soak the beans overnight in plenty of cold water.

Drain, cover with fresh water, and bring to the boil. Boil for 15 minutes, then change the water again. Add the celery and potatoes and simmer until cooked, about 30 minutes. When cooked, add salt. Mix in the olive oil, lemon and parsley.

Serve with black olives, onion slices and fresh crusty bread.

Anginares and Koukia
Artichokes with Fresh Broad Beans

SERVES 4

2 lb (900 g) fresh broad beans in their shells
4 globe artichokes
juice of 1½ lemons
1 medium onion, peeled and sliced thinly
1 tbsp olive oil
5 fl oz (150 ml) water
salt and pepper
2 tbsp finely chopped parsley

Shell the broad beans, discarding the pods of the large ones, but keeping the small and more tender pods whole. String the tender pods, wash them in cold water, then strain.

Prepare the artichokes by removing all the leaves, trimming the bases and scooping out the hairy chokes in the middle with a teaspoon. Rub all cut edges with a third of the lemon juice, and put into cold water.

Sauté the onion in the olive oil for 3–4 minutes, then add the remaining lemon juice and the water. Bring to the boil, then add the broad beans, small bean pods, artichokes, salt and pepper. Cover and cook gently for about 30–45 minutes (do not *over*cook).

Drain and sprinkle with parsley.

List of Restaurants

The Angel Inn, Bicester Road, Long Crendon, Aylesbury, Buckinghamshire HP018 9EE. Tel: (0844) 208268

Arts Theatre Cafe, 6 Great Newport Street, London WC2H 7JD. Tel: 071-497 8014

Bar Gansa, 2 Inverness Street, London NW1 7HJ. Tel: 071-267 8909

Ben's Thai Restaurant, 93 Warrington Crescent, London W9. Tel: 071-266 3134

Bertorelli's, 44a Floral Street, London WC2E 9DA. Tel: 071-836 3969

Blue Elephant, 4 Fulham Broadway, London SW6 1AA. Tel: 071-385 6595

Cafe Fish, 39 Panton Street, London SW1Y 4DN. Tel: 071-930 3999

The Canteen, Chelsea Harbour, London SW3. Tel: 071-351 7330

Daphne's, 83 Bayham Street, London NW1 0AG. Tel: 071-267 7322

dell'Ugo, 56 Frith Street, London W1V 5TA. Tel: 071-734 8300

The Greenhouse, 27a Hay's Mews, London W1X 7RA. Tel: 071-499 3331

Le Manoir aux Quat' Saisons, Great Milton, Oxfordshire OX9 7PD. Tel: (0844) 278881

McCoy's Tontine, Staddlebridge, Nr Northallerton, N. Yorkshire DL6 3JB. Tel: (0609) 82671

Millers, 1 Montpelier Mews, Harrogate, Yorkshire HG1 2TG. Tel: (0423) 530708

Nico at Ninety, 90 Park Lane, London W1A 3AA. Tel: 071-409 1290

The Olive Tree, 11 Wardour Street, London W1V 3HE. Tel: 071-734 0808

The Provence, Gordelton Mill Hotel, Silver Street, Hordle, Lymington, Hampshire SO41 6DJ. Tel: (0590) 682219

St James Court Hotel, Buckingham Gate, London SW1E 6AF. Tel: 071-834 6655

Soho Soho, 11–13 Frith Street, London W1V 5TS. Tel: 071-494 3491

The Square, 32 King Street, London SW1Y 6RJ. Tel: 071-839 8787

Zen NW3, 83 High Street, Hampstead, London NW3 2ER. Tel: 071-794 7863

Further Reading

BOOKS

Blanc, Raymond. *Le Manoir aux Quat' Saisons*. Macdonald 1988.

Bonino, Maddalena. *The Festive Food of Italy*. Kyle Cathie 1991.

Burkitt, Dr Denis. *Don't Forget Fibre in Your Diet*. Martin Dunitz 1983.

Cannon, Geoffrey. *Food and Health – The Experts Agree*. Consumers' Association 1992.

Complete Guide to Cookery. Reader's Digest Association 1989.

Coronary Prevention Group. *Preventing Heart Disease*. Consumers' Association and Hodder & Stoughton 1991.

David, Elizabeth. *French Provincial Cookery*. Michael Joseph 1965 and Penguin 1986.

Dolamore, Anne. *The Essential Olive Oil Companion*. Grub Street 1988.

The Drink Pocket Book 1992. NTC Publications 1992.

Eat Better, Live Better: The Family Guide to Healthy Eating. Reader's Digest Association 1991.

Eylaud, Dr Jean Max. *Vin et Santé*. La Diffusion Nouvelle du Livre 1960.

Good Housekeeping with the Coronary Prevention Group. *Eating for a Healthy Heart*. Ebury Press 1988.

Hewitson, Don. *Enjoying Wine*. Trafalgar 1987.

Independent Food and Drink. The Official Yearbook of the British Independent Grocers' Association 1991/92.

Johnson, Hugh. *Hugh Johnson's Pocket Wine Book*. Mitchell Beazley 1992.

Keys, Ancel and Margaret. *Eat Well and Stay Well*. Hodder & Stoughton 1960.

Lake, Mark and Ridgway, Judy. *Pocket Guide to Oils, Vinegars and Seasonings*. Mitchell Beazley 1989.

Loftus, Simon. *Anatomy of the Wine Trade*. Sidgwick & Jackson 1985.

Longstaff, Roberta and Mann, Jim. *The Healthy Heart Diet Book*. Martin Dunitz 1986.

Robinson, Jancis. *On the Demon Drink*. Mitchell Beazley 1988.

Sanders, Dr Tom and Bazalgette, Peter. *The Food Revolution*. Bantam Press 1991.

Scaravelli, Vita. *Awakening the Spine*. Aquarian Press 1991.

Sevilla, Maria José. *Life and Food in the Basque Country*. Weidenfeld 1989.

REPORTS AND ARTICLES

Diet and Cardiovascular Disease: A Report by the Committee on Medical Aspects of Food Policy. Department of Health and Social Security. HMSO 1984.

A Discussion Paper on Proposals for Nutritional Guidelines for Health Education in Britain. Health Education Council. NACNE 1983.

Family Spending: A Report on the 1990 Family Expenditure Survey. Central Statistical Office. HMSO 1990.

The Food Magazine. February/March 1992.

The Health of the Nation. Department of Health. HMSO 1992.

The Lancet. 20 June 1992.

Taste. April 1992 and July 1992.

Weekend Guardian. 11–12 July 1992.

The Wine Spectator. 31 December 1991 and 15 July 1992.

Index

A selection of bestsellers from Headline

FICTION

STUDPOKER	John Francome	£4.99 □
DANGEROUS LADY	Martina Cole	£4.99 □
TIME OFF FROM GOOD BEHAVIOUR	Susan Sussman	£4.99 □
THE KEY TO MIDNIGHT	Dean Koontz	£4.99 □
LEGAL TENDER	Richard Smitten	£5.99 □
BLESSINGS AND SORROWS	Christine Thomas	£4.99 □
VAGABONDS	Josephine Cox	£4.99 □
DAUGHTER OF TINTAGEL	Fay Sampson	£5.99 □
HAPPY ENDINGS	Sally Quinn	£5.99 □
BLOOD GAMES	Richard Laymon	£4.99 □
EXCEPTIONAL CLEARANCE	William J Caunitz	£4.99 □
QUILLER BAMBOO	Adam Hall	£4.99 □

NON-FICTION

RICHARD BRANSON: The Inside Story	Mick Brown	£6.99 □
PLAYFAIR FOOTBALL ANNUAL 1992-93	Jack Rollin	£3.99 □
DEBRETT'S ETIQUETTE & MODERN MANNERS	Elsie Burch Donald	£7.99 □
PLAYFIELD NON-LEAGUE FOOTBALL ANNUAL 1992-93	Bruce Smith	£3.99 □

SCIENCE FICTION AND FANTASY

THE CINEVERSE CYCLE OMNIBUS	Craig Shaw Gardner	£5.99 □
BURYING THE SHADOW	Storm Constantine	£4.99 □
THE LOST PRINCE	Bridget Wood	£5.99 □
KING OF THE DEAD	R A MacAvoy	£4.50 □
THE ULTIMATE WEREWOLF	Byron Preiss	£4.99 □

All Headline books are available at your local bookshop or newsagent, or can be ordered direct from the publisher. Just tick the titles you want and fill in the form below. Prices and availability subject to change without notice.

Headline Book Publishing PLC, Cash Sales Department, PO Box 11, Falmouth, Cornwall, TR10 9EN, England.

Please enclose a cheque or postal order to the value of the cover price and allow the following for postage and packing:
UK & BFPO: £1.00 for the first book, 50p for the second book and 30p for each additional book ordered up to a maximum charge of £3.00.
OVERSEAS & EIRE: £2.00 for the first book, £1.00 for the second book and 50p for each additional book.

Name ....

Address ....

....